CLASSIC RESEARCHES IN GENERAL CHEMISTRY

Series Editor · HAROLD HART, MICHIGAN STATE UNIVERSITY

THE

CLASSIC RESEARCHES IN GENERAL CHEMISTRY

J. J. LAGOWSKI · THE UNIVERSITY OF TEXAS

CHEMICAL

BOND

HOUGHTON MIFFLIN COMPANY · BOSTON

NEW YORK · ATLANTA · GENEVA, ILL. · DALLAS · PALO ALTO

To J

also

Cover photo: The spatial relationship between the atoms in a molecule as well as between the molecules in a crystal can be determined by X-ray diffraction techniques. X-ray data yield electron density contour maps which show the positions of the atoms, the contour lines being close together in the vicinity of an atom. The electron density map and position of the atoms in a crystal of potassium isocitric lactone are shown. (Courtesy of Glusker, Patterson, Love, and Dornberg, *Acta Crystallographica,* **16,** 1104 (1963).)

EDITOR'S INTRODUCTION

The accelerated pace of scientific discovery which characterizes our time has necessarily eliminated the historical approach to the study of science. Elementary texts in chemistry and physics cannot detail the often tortuous arguments, hypotheses, and experiments upon which currently accepted theories and facts are built. The result is frequently an outline of where we stand today, with only a few cogent arguments or supporting experiments enumerated. During the continuous distillation and condensation (which, indeed, are necessary to prevent elementary texts from becoming encyclopedic), many discoveries, when described in textbook fashion, lose their freshness.

But scientific discovery is a thrilling and exciting process, and a zest for it should be imparted to the beginning student. This series of paperbacks was initiated with the view that much might be done toward this end if the beginner could read about key discoveries in science in the words of the men who wrote of them. The research worker who contributes to the advancing front of science must read of discoveries as they appear in the scientific journals; he cannot wait until they become the subject matter of textbooks. It would seem advisable, then, to introduce the neophyte to the original literature as early in his scientific career as possible. The difficulty encountered in doing this lies in the student's lack of a suitable background necessary for him to profit from being turned loose amongst the journals with a list of references to read. Indeed, he may be dissuaded altogether from the sciences if subjected to such a "trial by fire" procedure. It was therefore decided that original papers, or portions thereof, be selected and presented with sufficient editorial comment to set the stage for each paper and to clarify passages which might be troublesome to the beginner. For the most part, the great scientists are allowed to speak for themselves.

The non-science major who takes a year of college chemistry or physics as part of his liberal education will find that this little book makes fascinating reading not only because the scientists come alive on its pages, but also because he can learn much about the use of logic and scientific method. But foremost, this book will make excellent supplementary reading for the professional student of chemistry or physics who wants to understand in greater detail the basis for our modern theories of chemical bonding.

HAROLD HART

v

PREFACE

In accordance with the procedure established in the first volume of this series, an attempt has been made to organize those investigations and ideas which have contributed to our knowledge and understanding of the nature of the chemical bond. The investigators' own words have been used where possible, although some of the more modern concepts are presented in a condensed form because of space limitations: in these instances references to more detailed discussions are provided in the "Suggested Reading" list.

It was not possible to quote all the important papers which pertain to the subject or even the entire text of those papers chosen for inclusion. A rather arbitrary choice was made in several instances where more than one investigator was active in the field. In these cases an attempt was made to point out the contributions of those scientists whose papers could not be included, and I must apologize in advance for any oversights which I may have committed in preparing this volume.

I wish to express my appreciation to the staff at the Houghton Mifflin Company for their untiring assistance during the preparation of this volume; to Professor Hart, the editor of this series, for his helpful criticisms of the manuscript; to Mr. E. S. Bradley of the Physics Library, The University of Texas, for his invaluable assistance; to Mr. A. E. Skinner of the Chemistry Library, The University of Texas, for generously providing his expertise on a variety of subjects; and most of all, to my wife, Jeanne, for her never-ending encouragement and for her critique of this volume.

The permission of the publishers of the original works which are represented in part in this volume is gratefully acknowledged.

J. J. L.
Austin, Texas

CONTENTS

	Editor's Introduction	v
	Preface	vi
1	Early Theories of Atomic Combinations	1
2	Affinity	9
3	Structure	31
4	Three-Dimensional Chemistry	57
5	The Elements and Their Compounds: Periodicity	64
6	Electrons and Atomic Structure	70
7	Electrons and Periodicity	79
8	The Structural Units of Matter	118
9	The Electrical Nature of the Chemical Bond	131
10	Electron Pairs and Geometry	146
11	Electrons and Waves	164
12	The Chemical Bond	183
	Epilogue	197
	Index	198

CHAPTER 1

Early Theories of

Atomic Combination

The existence of atoms and the more complex units of matter comprised of atoms leads naturally to a consideration of the relationship which exists between the fundamental units and their aggregates. We know, for example, that chlorine gas (Cl_2) reacts with hydrogen gas (H_2), sodium metal (Na), and carbon (C) to form hydrogen chloride (HCl), sodium chloride (NaCl), and carbon tetrachloride (CCl_4), respectively. The physical and chemical properties of hydrogen, chlorine, hydrogen chloride, and carbon tetrachloride as a group are markedly different from those of sodium chloride, which in turn differ from those of sodium and carbon, yet all of these substances are composed of aggregates of atoms. These simple observations lead to questions concerning (a) the combining ratios of the atoms that form the aggregates, (b) the geometry of the aggregates, and (c) the nature of the forces which hold the atoms in aggregation. It is an experimental fact that the atom ratio of the elements in sodium chloride and in hydrogen chloride is 1:1, whereas in carbon tetrachloride it is 1:4. However, our interest here concerns questions such as why one atom of hydrogen or one atom of sodium combines with one atom of chlorine while one atom of carbon combines with four atoms of chlorine. Why is chlorine diatomic and gaseous at room temperature and a non-conductor in the solid and liquid state whereas sodium forms a crystalline lattice under the same conditions and can conduct an electric current? Why, on the other hand, is sodium chloride, which also forms a crystalline lattice, a non-conductor in the solid state but a conductor in the molten state? It might appear that these questions could be answered if we understood the changes an atom undergoes when a chemical reaction occurs, the nature of the particles that constitute compounds, and the forces that hold these particles together. However, as we shall see, the question of how molecules are formed from atoms is still basically at issue in spite of numerous attempts to answer it.

MECHANICAL LINKAGES BETWEEN ATOMS

It should be recalled that the earliest philosophers were divided into two schools, according to their ideas concerning the nature of matter. Leucippus,[1] Democritus,[2] and Epicurus[3] thought matter to be particulate and were therefore forced to consider the manner in which the fundamental particles could interact to form the various kinds of matter which existed; on the other hand, those philosophers who thought matter to be continuous were not faced with this problem. The early atomists could draw only on simple observation and imagination to construct theories on the nature of how the fundamental particles combine. Often the theories put forth were picturesque in their details concerning the nature of atoms; consider, for example, the following contemporary commentary on Democritus' concept of chemical union.

▼   "The atoms are at war with one another as they move along in the void owing to their dissimilarity and their other differences, and as they move they collide and are interlaced in a manner which makes them touch and be near to one another, but never really produces any single existence out of them: for it is quite absurd to suppose that two or more things could ever become one. The reason why the atoms for a certain time remain in combination he (Democritus) believes to be because they fit into and grasp one another: for some of them have uneven sides, and some are hooked, some are concave, and some convex and others with innumerable varieties of shape. He (Democritus) thinks then that they retain hold of one another and remain in combination until some stronger necessity from what surrounds them comes and shakes them and scatters them apart.

[1] Leucippus (fifth century B.C.): Greek philosopher. He was credited by Aristotle with having been the originator of the theory of atomism. Briefly, Leucippus' theory states that (a) atoms are infinite in number and occupy an infinite space, (b) atoms are constantly in motion and in the ensuing collisions and entanglements form compound substances, (c) the atoms in compound substances are not in combination but are merely in juxtaposition, and (d) the differences between physical things arise from the shape, arrangement, and position of their constituent atoms.

[2] Democritus (460–370 B.C.): A Greek philosopher who extended the "mechanistic" philosophy of his teacher Leucippus. The atomic theory is an integral part of Democritus' philosophy and was based on reason rather than experiment.

[3] Epicurus (341–270 B.C.): Greek philosopher. Although primarily known for his teachings in ethics, Epicurus is also notable for his exposition of the atomic theory.

And he (Democritus) speaks of this coming into being and its opposite separation not merely with reference to animals, but also plants and worlds and generally about all perceptible bodies."[4]   ▲

Epicurus considered size, shape, and weight to be the three fundamental properties of atoms. Few of his writings that are directly concerned with the combination of atoms to yield other forms of matter have been preserved, but Epicurus' ideas survive in the works of his contemporaries. For example, LUCRETIUS attempts to describe in *De Rerum Natura* the gross differences observed between olive oil and wine by discussing the nature of the particles which constitute each of these substances.

▼   "And we see wine flow through the strainer as swiftly as you will; but, on the other hand, the sluggish olive-oil hangs back, because we may be sure, it is composed of particles either larger or more hooked and entangled one with the other, and so it comes about that the first-beginnings cannot so quickly be drawn apart, each single one from the rest, and so ooze through the single holes of each thing."[5]   ▲

LUCRETIUS continues his description of matter, attempting to explain the differences between solids, liquids, and gases.

▼   "Or, again, things which seem to us hard and compact, these, it must need be, are made of particles more hooked one to another, and are held together close-fastened at their roots, as it were by branching particles. First of all in this class diamond stones stand in the forefront of the fight, well used to despise all blows, and stubborn flints and the strength of hard iron, and brass sockets, which scream aloud as they struggle against the bolts. Those things indeed must be made of particles more round and smooth, which are liquid with a fluid body: for indeed a handful of poppyseed moves easily just as a draught of water; for the several round particles are not checked one by the other, and when struck, it will roll downhill just like water. Lastly, all things which you perceive flying asunder, like smoke, clouds and flames, it must needs be that even if they are not made entirely of smooth and round particles, yet they are not hampered by particles closely linked . . ."[6]   ▲

[4] As translated in *The Greek Atomists and Epicurus,* by Cyril Bailey (Oxford: The Clarendon Press, 1928), p. 136.
[5] LUCRETIUS, *De Rerum Natura,* trans. by Cyril Bailey (London: Oxford University Press, 1947), Book II, lines 391–407.
[6] *Ibid.,* lines 441–461.

Thus, it is apparent that the early thoughts on the constitution of matter were drawn by analogy from observations made on the macroscopic world, and it is not surprising that such mechanical devices as hooks (or the absence of hooks, i.e., smoothness) were invoked to explain the interactions of atoms. The concept of atoms was rejected by Aristotle,[7] who believed that matter was indefinitely divisible. This was unfortunate for the atomic theory, because Aristotelian philosophy was to remain the predominating influence on contemporary thought until the sixteenth century. With the increase of experimentation, interest in the atomic theory was revived. However, the concept of the union of atoms was still a mechanical one, as can be illustrated by the following excerpt from the works of the seventeenth century investigator John Mayow.[8]

▼   "For the same nitro-aerial particles which, when whirled around and hot, separated from each other the particles of these glowing substances and opened up their structure, now, when they cease to move in consequence of encountering cold, are fixed like wedges or very solid spikelets in their pores. Things are hardened by them when fixed in this manner, and indeed cold seems to close the pores of things in this way only."[9]   ▲

Mayow thus attempted to explain the formation of solid matter by bringing together particles bearing projections and indentations of the correct size; he invoked another mechanical device, "clasping hooks," to hold particles together. "And indeed, in my opinion frozen water differs from hardened iron chiefly in this, that the branching particles of iron adhere firmly to each other as though they were joined by clasping hooks, so that the nitroaerial spicules are more loosely interlaced with them."[10]

Although the anathema which the Greeks displayed for experimentation had been surmounted, the early chemists had only the results of crude and

[7] Aristotle (384–322 B.C.): A Greek philosopher, student of Plato, and teacher of Alexander the Great. Many of his ideas have survived the passage of time, but his suggestion that matter is infinite and the far-reaching influence of his ideas retarded the use of the experimental method.

[8] John Mayow (1640–1679): English physiologist and chemist. Mayow's most significant contribution to chemistry was his suggestion that air contains an "aerial spirit" which is necessary for the maintenance of life and for supporting combustion. Thus, a hundred years before Lavoisier, Mayow came very near to stating the theory of combustion for which Lavoisier is given credit.

[9] J. MAYOW, *Medico-Physical Works Being a Translation of Tractatus Quinque Medico-Physici*, Alembic Club Reprint, No. 17 (Edinburgh: Oliver and Boyd, 1907), p. 47.

[10] *Ibid.*, p. 50.

subjective observations upon which to formulate their theories. Lemery's[11] discourse on the relationships between acids, bases, and salts admirably illustrates the arguments that were used to describe the microscopic properties of individual atoms.

▼ ". . . . I shall affirm, that the *Acidity* of any Liquor does consist in keen Particles of *Salts,* put in motion; and I hope no Body will offer to dispute whether an *acid* has Points or no, seeing every ones Experience does demonstrate it, they need but taste an *Acid* to be satisfied of it, for it pricks the Tongue like any thing keen, and finely cut; but a demonstrative and convincing Proof that an *Acid* does consist of pointed Parts is, that not only all *acid Salts* do *Crystallize* into Edges, but all Dissolutions of different things, caused by *acid* Liquors, do assume this Figure in their *Crystallization;* these *Crystals* consist of Points differing both in Length and Bigness one from another, and this diversity must be attributed to the keener or blunter Edges of the different Sorts of *Acids.*

"As for *Alkali's,* they are soon known by pouring an *acid* upon them, for presently or soon after, there rises a violent *Ebullition,* which remains until the *acid* finds no more bodies to rarifie. This effect may make us reasonably conjecture that an *Alkali* is a terrestrious and solid matter, whose *pores* are figured after such a manner that the *acid* points entering into them do strike and divide whatsoever opposes their motion. . . .

"There are as many different *Alkali's,* as there are bodies that have different pores, and this is the reason why an *acid* will Ferment with one strongly, and with another not at all; for there must be a due proportion between the *acid* points, and the *pores* of the *Alkali.*"[12] ▲

Lemery's suggestion that acids are particles with spikes on their surface because of the pricking sensation they give to the tongue is an extension of the type of argument used by Democritus earlier. Lemery had the advantage of having a larger number of observations on which to base his model to explain acid-base reactions. It is interesting to note that he anticipated the equivalence of acids and bases when he mentioned the "due proportion of acid points and the pores of the alkali."

[11] Nicolas Lemery (1645–1715): A French apothecary and doctor of medicine who was among the first to attempt to remove chemistry from the shadows of mysticism and reduce it to clear, simple ideas. He enjoyed great success as a teacher, and his book *Cours de Chymie* appeared in thirteen editions; it was translated into Latin, English, German, and Spanish and became the instrument by which his ideas were spread throughout the Western world.

[12] N. LEMERY, *A Course in Chemistry,* 4th English ed. (London: Printed for A. Bell and others, 1720), pp. 13–14.

It must have been apparent to the early experimenters that chemical reactions were sometimes vigorous, sometimes sluggish, and sometimes incomplete; the idea arose that chemical reactions occurred because the combining substances were alike in some manner. Albertus Magnus wrote that "sulphur destroys the metals because of its natural affinity to them."[13] He was trying to convey the observation that it is very difficult to recover the metal after a reaction has occurred. The early chemistry attributed qualities normally associated with the human mind to material substances. For example, Glauber states that "sand and its like have a great community with the salt of tartar[14] and they love each other very much, so that neither of them willingly parts from the other."[15] However, Boyle[16] protested against bestowing such attributes on inanimate bodies.

▼ "I am dissatisfied with the very fundamental notion of this doctrine, namely a supposed hostility between the tribe of acids and that of alkalies, accompanied, if you will have it so, with a friendship or sympathy with bodies belonging to the same tribe or family. For I look upon amity and enmity as affections of intelligent beings; and I have not yet found it explained by any, how those appetites can be placed in bodies inanimate and devoid of knowledge or of so much as sense."[17]   ▲

FORCES OF ATTRACTION BETWEEN ATOMS

The concept that chemical affinity is the attractive force, exerted in different degrees between different atoms, which causes atoms to enter into and remain in combination was probably first clearly stated by Isaac Newton.[18]

▼ "Have not the small Particles of Bodies certain Powers, Virtues or Forces, by which they act at a distance, not only upon the Rays of Light

[13] J. M. STILLMAN, *The Story of Early Chemistry* (New York: D. Appleton and Company, 1924), p. 499.

[14] K_2CO_3.

[15] *Ibid.*

[16] Robert Boyle (1626/7–1691): Youngest son of the Earl of Cork, chemist, natural philosopher, amateur of medicine and theology, essayist, and linguist. Along with Bacon, Galileo, and Newton, Boyle led the attack on the Aristotelian concept of nature and was one of the early successful practitioners of experimental natural philosophy. His influence on chemistry was extensive because he was among the first to include the study of chemistry in natural philosophy when the former was generally considered as either a mystic science or a practical art.

[17] *The Works of The Honourable Robert R. Boyle,* Vol. III (London: Printed for A. Millar, 1744), p. 603.

[18] Sir Isaac Newton (1642–1727): English mathematician and natural philosopher. Although known principally for his investigations in physics and mathematics, Newton's ideas on the forces of attraction between the units comprising compounds were essentially correct.

for reflecting, refracting and inflecting them, but also upon one another for producing a great part of the Phenomena of Nature? For it's well known that Bodies act one upon another by the attractions of Gravity, Magnetism and Electricity; and instances show that Tenor and Course of Nature, and make it not improbable but that there may be more attractive Powers than these. For Nature is very consonant and conformable to herself. How these Attractions may be performed, I do not here consider. What I call attraction may be performed by impulse, or by some other means unknown to me. I use that Word here to signify only in general any Force by which Bodies tend towards one another, whatsoever be the Cause. For we must learn from the Phaenomena of Nature what Bodies attract one another, and what are the Laws and Properties of Attraction, before we enquire the Cause by which the Attraction is performed. The Attractions of Gravity, Magnetism and Electricity, reach to very sensible distances, and so have been observed by vulgar Eyes, and there may be others which reach to so small distances as hitherto escape Observation; and perhaps electrical Attraction may reach to such small distances, even without being excited by Friction.

"For when Salt of Tartar runs *per deliquium*[19] is not this done by an Attraction between the Particles of the Salt of Tartar, and the Particles of the Water which float in the Air in the form of Vapours? And why does not Common Salt, or Saltpeter,[20] or Vitriol,[21] run *per deliquium,* but for want of such an attraction? Or why does not Salt of Tartar draw more Water out of the Air than in a certain Proportion to its quantity, but for want of an attractive Force after it is satiated with Water? And whence is it but from this attractive Power that Water which alone distils with a gentle lukewarm Heat, will not distil from the Salt of Tartar without a great Heat? . . . The parts of all homogeneal hard Bodies which fully touch one another, stick together very strongly. And for explaining how this may be, some have invented hooked Atoms, which is begging the Question; and others tell us that Bodies are glued together by rest, that is by an occult Quality, or rather by nothing; and others, that they stick together by conspiring Motions, that is by relative rest among themselves. I had rather infer from their Cohesion, that their Particles attract one another by some Force, which in immediate Contact is exceeding strong, at small distances performs the chymical Operations above mentioned, and reaches not far from the Particles with any sensible Effect."[22]   ▲

---

[19] Deliquesces.
[20] KNO_3.
[21] H_2SO_4.
[22] I. NEWTON, *Opticks,* 2nd ed. (London: Printed for W. and J. Inny, 1718), pp. 350 ff.

In essence, Newton rejected the mechanical contrivances of hooks, glue, and the like and suggested that the forces holding atoms together in complex arrangements might be electrical in nature. Newton in his genius was essentially correct! It was another two hundred years before any further appreciable progress was made in this area. During those two centuries chemists expended their efforts in attempting to understand the chemistry of a seemingly bewildering variety of substances and to develop structural concepts before they returned to a consideration of Newton's suggestions.

SUGGESTED READING

Coward, H. F. "John Dalton's Lecture Diagrams on the Atomic Theory," *Journal of Chemical Education,* **4,** 23 (1927).

Gillespie, C. C. "A Physicist Looks at Greek Science," *American Scientist,* **46,** 62 (1958).

Gorman, M. "Philosophical Antecedents of the Modern Atom," *Journal of Chemical Education,* **37,** 100 (1960).

Parravano, N. "Cannizzaro and the Atomic Theory," *Journal of Chemical Education,* **4,** 836 (1927).

Scott, J. H. "The Nineteenth Century Atom; Undivided or Indivisible," *Journal of Chemical Education,* **36,** 64 (1959).

CHAPTER 2

Affinity

The enunciation of the concept of affinity initiated a confusing sequence of events in which chemists attempted both to measure this property and to describe its origin. Unfortunately, accomplishing the latter task required an understanding of the proportions in which atoms combine, structural concepts, and the electrical constitution of atoms. Only then could a meaningful description of the nature of the aggregation of atoms into more complex units be developed. Until these factors were understood, all of the suggestions concerning the origin of affinity were necessarily vague and impossible to prove experimentally. Thus in 1778, Buffon,[1] the French naturalist, suggested that the phenomenon of chemical affinity arose from gravitational forces as modified by the varying shapes of the combining particles as well as by the small distances between the particles.

TABLES OF AFFINITY

The early chemists recognized that a given substance combined with other substances more or less readily, and the idea arose that this variation in reactivity could be used as a measure of the force of attraction between the reacting units. The first attempt to measure the relative affinities of substances on this basis was made by Étienne-François Geoffroy,[2] who sought to systematize the results of his experiments as well as those of other chemists.

[1] Georges Louis Leclerc, Comte de Buffon (1707–1788): French naturalist. In his sweeping work, *Natural History,* Buffon attempted to present an account of the phenomena of nature and included a variety of chemical subjects.
[2] Étienne-François Geoffroy (1672–1731): Professor, Collège de France. His major contribution to chemistry was a detailed study of the reactions of acids and bases with metals, the results of which contributed to the development of the first tables of affinities.

9

GEOFFROY presented his ideas to the Royal Academy of Sciences at Paris on August 27, 1718.

▼   "We observe in chemistry certain affinities between different bodies according to which they unite easily, one with another. These affinities have their degrees and are governed by their laws. We observe their different degrees when, among many mixed materials which have some disposition to unite, we note that one of the substances invariably unites with a certain other one in preference to all the rest.

"For the laws of these affinities I have observed that when two substances having a disposition to unite together are combined and a third added, the third may part the two, taking one or the other. Some other substances neither join with the one or the other and do not lessen them at all. From this it appears to me that we may with some certainty conclude that those substances which were joined to one of the two had more affinity of union or disposition to unite to it than the substances which were displaced, and I believe that one can deduce from these observations the following proposition which is very general, although one cannot give it as general without having examined all possible combinations to assure that there is nothing to the contrary.

"Whenever two substances which have some disposition to unite, the one with the other, are united together and a third which has more affinity for one of the two is added, the third will unite with one of these, separating it from the other.

"This proposition is very general in chemistry where one encounters, so to speak at every step, the effects of this affinity. It is this property upon which depends the greater part of the hidden movements which follow the mixing of bodies and which are nearly impenetrable without this key. But since the order of these affinities is little known, I have believed that it would be very useful to mark those affinities which the substances commonly met with in chemistry show to each other and to construct a table where at a glance one could see the different affinities which substances have for one another."[3]   ▲

Geoffroy summarized his results along with those of other chemists in tabular form (see facing page). At the head of each column appears the symbol of a substance which will react with every substance listed below it in decreasing "order of affinity." The table and its significance are best described in GEOFFROY'S own words.

[3] *Mémoires de l'Académie Royale des Sciences* (1718); trans. in H. M. Leicester and H. S. Klickstein, *A Source Book in Chemistry* (New York: McGraw-Hill Book Company, Inc., 1952; Cambridge: Harvard University Press, 1963), p. 67. Hereafter cited as *Source Book*.

▼   "The first line of this table includes different substances used in chemistry. Below each substance different types of materials are arranged in columns in the order of their affinity for that substance such that that which is nearest has the greatest affinity for the substance and cannot be displaced by any of the materials below it, but that it may remove any of the lower ones when they are joined to the substance. Thus in the first

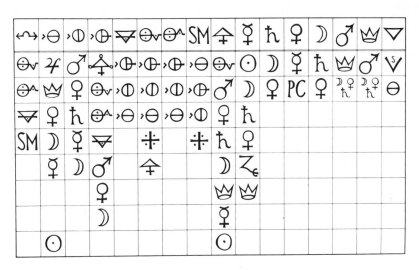

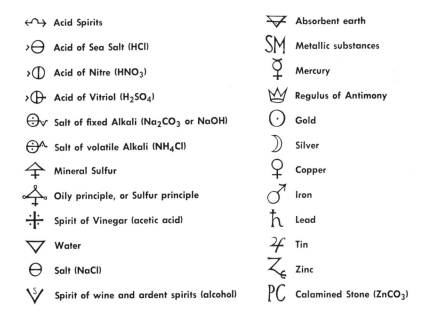

↩↪ Acid Spirits	▽ Absorbent earth
>⊖ Acid of Sea Salt (HCl)	SM Metallic substances
>① Acid of Nitre (HNO₃)	☿ Mercury
>⊕ Acid of Vitriol (H₂SO₄)	♛ Regulus of Antimony
⊖⌄ Salt of fixed Alkali (Na₂CO₃ or NaOH)	⊙ Gold
⊖ᴧ Salt of volatile Alkali (NH₄Cl)	☽ Silver
⚍ Mineral Sulfur	♀ Copper
⚍ Oily principle, or Sulfur principle	♂ Iron
╪ Spirit of Vinegar (acetic acid)	♄ Lead
▽ Water	♃ Tin
⊖ Salt (NaCl)	⚏ Zinc
ᐺ Spirit of wine and ardent spirits (alcohol)	PC Calamined Stone (ZnCO₃)

column the acid spirits are the substances with which I compare the four other kinds of substances which are below, that is, the fixed alkali salts, the volatile alkali salts, the absorbent earths, and metallic substances."[4]   ▲

It should be noted that Geoffroy's tables, and others based on his principles, did not necessarily reflect the affinity of atoms for each other in Newton's sense, i.e., a "Force by which Bodies tend towards one another, whatsoever be the Cause." Few of the substances in Geoffroy's table were elemental. Inspection of the table indicates that a variety of reaction types were included which logically cannot be interrelated; Berzelius later showed that the courses of reactions of this type are determined by the properties of the reactants, such as the formation of insoluble products, gaseous substances, or weakly ionized substances. However, the table represents one of the first attempts to systematize chemical knowledge. As GEOFFROY pointed out,

▼   "By this table those who are beginning to learn chemistry may form in a short time an adequate idea of the affinities which exist between different substances, and the chemists will there find an easy method to determine what takes place in many of their operations which are difficult to disentangle and to predict what should result when they mix different bodies."[5]

▲

To his credit, it should be mentioned that GEOFFROY recognized that his reactions were not complete, but he passed this off as an experimental difficulty which did not invalidate his results.

▼   "It should be noted that in many of these experiments the separation of materials is not perfectly exact and precise. This arises from several causes which are impossible to eliminate, such as the viscosity of the liquid, its movement, the character of the precipitant or precipitate, and other such things which prevent a prompt precipitation or an exact separation of all the parts. These errors are nevertheless not so large as to prevent one from regarding the rules as constant."[6]   ▲

Although Geoffroy did not succeed in his ultimate goal of measuring the affinity between atoms, his table did permit chemists to predict the course of reactions between substances.

[4] *Ibid.,* p. 68.
[5] *Ibid.*
[6] *Ibid.,* p. 74.

THE REFINEMENT OF THE AFFINITY TABLES

Geoffroy's tables of affinity were improved by the Swedish chemist Bergman,[7] who recognized that the course of chemical reactions was affected by temperature as well as by other considerations. BERGMAN distinguished between displacement reactions ("single elective attractions") and double decomposition reactions ("double attractions") as follows:

▼   "Several species of contiguous attraction may be distinguished. I shall here briefly mention the principal. When homogeneous bodies tend to union, an increase of mass only takes place, the nature of the body remaining still the same; and this effect is denominated the *attraction of aggregation*. But heterogeneous substances, when mixed together, and left to themselves to form combinations, are influenced by difference of quality rather than of quantity. This we call *attraction of composition;* and when it is exerted in forming a mere union of two or more substances, it receives the name of *attraction of solution* or *fusion,* according as it is effected either in the moist or the dry way. When it takes place between three respectively, to the exclusion of one, it is said to be a *single elective attraction;* when between two compounds, each consisting of only two proximate principles, which are exchanged in consequence of mixture, it is intitled *double attraction.* I am particularly to consider the two last species.

"Suppose *A* to be a substance for which other heterogeneous substances *a, b, c,* &c have an attraction; suppose further, *A* combined with *c* to saturation, (this union I shall call *Ac*), should, upon the addition of *b,* tend to unite with it to the exclusion of *c, A* is then said to attract *b* more strongly than *c,* or to have a stronger elective attraction of it; lastly, let the union of *Ab* on the addition of *a,* be broken, let *b* be rejected, and *a* chosen in its place, it will follow, that *a* exceeds *b* in attractive power, and we shall have a series, *a,b,c,* in respect of efficacy. What I here call attraction, others denominate affinity; I shall employ both terms promiscuously in the sequel, though the latter, being more metaphorical, would seem less proper in philosophy."[8]   ▲

Bergman's method for establishing the order of affinities for substances was based on the identification of a new substance when it was formed, and he took advantage of a variety of properties to follow the course of a reaction. The details of BERGMAN's method are best presented in his own words.

---

[7] Torbern Olof Bergman (1735–1784): Professor of Chemistry at Upsala. Bergman is primarily noted for his research in mineralogy, and for his famous essay on "Elective Affinities," which was the first attempt at systematizing chemistry.

[8] T. BERGMAN, *A Dissertation on Elective Attractions,* trans. by Edmund Cullen (London: J. Murray, 1785), pp. 5–9.

▼   "Suppose *a, b, c, d,* &c to be different substances, of which the attractive forces for *A* are to be ascertained.

"Let *Ad,* (i.e., *A* saturated with *d,*) be dissolved in distilled water, and then add a small quantity of *c,* which may either be soluble in water by itself or not. First let it be soluble; then a concentrated solution ought to be employed, which, when dropped into a solution of *Ad,* sometimes immediately affords a precipitate, which, being collected and washed, either proves to be a new combination, *Ac,* with peculiar properties, or *d* is extruded, or sometimes both. It now remains to be examined, whether the whole of *d* can be dislodged by a sufficient quantity of *c* from its former union. It should be carefully noted in general, that there is occasion for twice, thrice, nay sometimes six times the quantity of the decomponent *c,* than is necessary for saturating *A* when uncombined. If *c* effect no separation, not even in several hours, let the liquor stand to crystallize, or at least become dry by a spontaneous evaporation; high degrees of heat must be avoided, less they disturb the affinities. Here the knowledge of the form, taste, solubility, tendency to effloresce, and other properties, even those which, in other respects, appear of no consequence, of the substances, is of great use in enabling us to judge safely and readily, whether any, and what decomposition has taken place. Sometimes the disengaged substance, whether that which was added or expelled, gives the operator much trouble, by concealing the genuine properties of the other, and therefore, if possible, should be removed, according to circumstances, either by water or spirit of wine."[9]   ▲

The reactions which Bergman studied (1) yielded, or were made to yield, precipitates, (2) involved displacement of one metal by another, or (3) produced easily volatile substances. We now know that the course of these reactions is dependent upon the experimental conditions in relation to the properties of the reactants. Thus, for example, a substance which is soluble in water could be precipitated by the addition of alcohol. It is apparent from our present knowledge that the affinities determined using these methods had little significance.

BERGMAN realized the difficulty in preparing tables incorporating the results of reactions between all the known substances when he stated:

▼   "By such an examination properly conducted, the order of attractions is discovered. This task, however, exercises all the patience, and diligence, and accuracy, and knowledge, and experience of the chemist. Let us suppose only a series of five terms, *a, b, c, d,* and *e,* to be examined with respect to *A,* twenty different experiments are requisite, of which each in-

[9] *Ibid.,* pp. 64–67.

volves several others: a series of ten terms requires ninety experiments, and, in general, if a be the number of the series, $n \cdot n - 1$ will be the number of experiments.

"The tables which we have at present contain only a few substances, and each of these compared only a with a few others. This is no reproach to the authors of them, for the task is laborious and long. Although, therefore, I have been employed upon it with all the diligence I could exert, and as much as my many other engagements would permit, yet I am very far from venturing to assert, that that which I offer is perfect, since I know with certainty, that the slight sketch now proposed will require above 30,000 exact experiments before it can be brought to any degree of perfection. But when I reflected on the shortness of life, and the instability of health, I resolved to publish my observations, however defective, lest they should perish with my papers, and I shall relate them as briefly as possible. In itself it is of small consequence by whom science is enriched; whether the truths belonging to it are discovered by me or by another. Meanwhile, if God shall grant me life, health, and the necessary leisure, I will persevere in the task which I have begun."[10] ▲

The tables of affinity which Bergman published distinguished between reactions which occurred in water at ordinary temperatures ("the wet way") and those which occurred at high temperatures ("the dry way"). He recognized that a change in temperature could change the course of a reaction, but he wrongly interpreted this to mean a change in the affinities or the forces of attraction between the substances involved. An attempt was made by BERGMAN to use this change to place the concept of affinity on a quantitative basis.

▼ "The only external condition, which either weakens or totally inverts the affinities of bodies subjected to experiments, is the different intensity of heat. But this cause can only operate in cases where the same temperature renders some bodies remarkably volatile in comparison of others.

"Suppose A to be attracted by two other substances; and let the more powerful act at the ordinary temperature with the force a, the weaker with the force b: suppose at the same time, the former to be the more volatile; let its effort to arise be expressed by V, and that of the other by v. When these three substances are mixed together, the stronger will attract A with a force $= a - b$: but should the heat be gradually raised, this superior force will be more and more diminished; and as V will increase faster than v, we shall at last have $a - b = V - v$. This state of equilibrium will be immediately destroyed by the smallest addition of heat; and thus b, which

[10] *Ibid.*, pp. 68–70.

was before the weaker, and incapable of producing any effect, will now prevail. If the other substance be entirely of a fixed nature, $v = o,$ and the case will be simpler. Many instances of this nature will hereafter occur."[11]

▲

It is apparent that Bergman was attempting to show the balance of forces which can exist between reacting units of a given affinity. Unfortunately, the methods chosen to measure relative affinities reflected more the factors which affect the position of chemical equilibria. He was convinced that the true affinities of substances were those measured at room temperature, although he recognized that the order of affinity could change with temperature. BERG-MAN thus prepared two affinity tables, one for "the wet way" and one for "the dry way."

▼   "Hence, I think it in general obvious, that those are the genuine attractions, which take place when bodies are left to themselves: too high a degree of heat is an external cause, which forcibly weakens the real affinities more or less, nay, in some cases, even totally alters them. Since, however, many operations cannot be carried on without the aid of heat, and the power therefore of this most subtile fluid is highly worthy of being observed, I think the table of elective attractions ought to be divided into two areas; of which the upper may exhibit the free attractions, that take place in the moist way, as the expression is; and the lower, those which are effected by the force of heat. This may easily be done, since we are as yet unacquainted with any other external condition which deserves here to be taken into the account; if the internal conditions ever cause any deviation, it is either only apparent, or else a real change in the nature of the substances is produced.

"It is hence evident, what opinion we are to form concerning the various arguments brought against the constancy of affinities, from the distillation, sublimation, or fusion of mixtures; such sometimes is the efficacy of heat, that strong digestion, or even that degree of warmth which is produced by the combination of certain substances, is sufficient to disturb the usual order."[12]

▲

FACTORS AFFECTING THE COURSE OF A REACTION

Although Bergman believed that the affinity of a substance, as measured by his method of "elective attraction," was constant, he realized that often an excess of one of the reactants was required to drive the reaction to com-

[11] *Ibid.,* p. 14.
[12] *Ibid.,* pp. 15–17.

pletion. It was Berthollet[13] who thought that the course of a reaction could be affected by factors such as solubility and volatility and suggested that the tables of affinity compiled by earlier chemists did not necessarily reflect the force of attraction between the reacting units. BERTHOLLET'S ideas on the subject are concisely summarized in a paper which is a model of expository clarity, the introduction of which follows.

▼   "A *theory* of chemical affinities solidly established, and serving as the basis for the explanation of all chemical questions, ought to be a collection of, or contain, all the principles from which the causes of chemical phenomena can proceed, in every possible variety of circumstance; because observation has proved, that all these phenomena are only the various effects of that affinity, to which all the various chemical powers of bodies may be attributed.

"It cannot be expected that a work of this nature should have attained the utmost degree of perfection within the short space of time which has elapsed since chemistry has become regularly and philosophically progressive.

"Bergman has treated this subject, and with more success than any other author. His work on elective affinity is useful and meritorious, not alone by the speculations which it contains on the nature of chemical affinities, on the opposition and concurrence of their various actions, and on the circumstances which can modify or disguise these actions: but still further, by the great number of chemical facts which it contains; and although observations have been made and multiplied since that great chemist wrote, and although some very learned treatises have been published on affinity since that time; yet his doctrine is that generally adopted. I have been determined by that consideration, to make his work the basis of the principal part of the discussions which follow.

"Let us suppose, says Bergman, the substance A completely saturated with the substance C, and that the combination be termed AC; if the addition of another substance, B, to this combination, removes C, there will result the combination AB, instead of AC. He prescribes then, for determining the elective affinity of two substances, to try if one of them can remove the other from its combination with a third, and *vice versa*.

[13] Claude Louis Berthollet (1748–1822): Professor at the École Normale. Born in humble circumstances, Berthollet filled many responsible positions in the government of France and eventually became a Count of the Empire under Napoleon. His belief that two or more elements could combine in varying proportions was the source of a long controversy with Proust during which the latter established the law of definite composition. Among his chemical accomplishments are the introduction of "Eau de Javelle" for bleaching purposes, the establishment of the composition of ammonia, hydrogen cyanide, and hydrogen sulfide, and the revision (with Lavoisier) of chemical nomenclature.

He takes it for granted, that that body which has removed another from its combination, cannot, in like manner, be expelled by that other, and that both experiments will concur to prove that the first has a greater elective affinity than the second. He adds at the same time, that it may be necessary to employ six times as much of the decomposing substance as would be necessary to saturate immediately the substance with which it tends to combine.

"The doctrine of Bergman is founded entirely on the supposition that elective affinity is an invariable force, and of such a nature, that a body which expels another from its combination, cannot possibly be separated from the same by the body which it eliminated.

"It is my purpose to prove in the following sheets, that elective affinity, in general, does not act as a determinate force, by which one body separates completely another from a combination; but that, in all the compositions and decompositions produced by elective affinity, there takes place a partition of the base, or subject of the combination, between the two bodies whose actions are opposed; and that the proportions of this partition are determined, not solely by the difference of energy in the affinities, but also by the difference of the quantities of the bodies; so that an excess of quantity of the body whose affinity is the weaker, compensates for the weakness of the affinity.

"If I can prove that a weaker degree of affinity can be compensated by an increase of quantity, it will follow, that the action of any body is proportionate to the quantity of it which is necessary to produce a certain degree of saturation. The quantity, which is the measure of the capacity of saturation of different bodies, I shall call *mass*.

"Hence it follows, that in estimating the comparative affinities of bodies, their absolute weights are to be considered, and ought to be equal; but in comparing their actions, which depend on their affinities and mutual proportions, the mass of each is to be considered.

"I shall prove, therefore, that, in opposing the body A to the combination BC, the combination AC can never take place; but that the body C will be divided between the bodies A and B, proportionally to the affinity and quantity of each; that is, to their respective masses."[14]   ▲

Berthollet then showed, by conducting a variety of experiments, that, in general, reactions do not necessarily go to completion spontaneously but that they can be made to go to completion by using an excess of one of the reactants.

[14] C. L. BERTHOLLET, *Researches into the Laws of Chemical Affinity,* trans. by M. Farrell (Baltimore: Printed for P. H. Nicklin, 1804); reprinted in *Source Book,* p. 193.

THE NATURE OF BERGMAN'S AFFINITY

The results of BERTHOLLET'S experiments led him to the conclusion which clearly distinguished between the nature of the affinity (supposedly measured in Bergman's tables) and the forces of attraction between reacting units.

▼   "It results then from the preceding experiments, many circumstances of which I shall examine in the sequel, that when a substance acts on a combination, the subject of combination divides itself between the two others, not only in proportion to the energy of their respective affinities, but also in proportion to their quantities. The two substances which act on the combination ought to be considered as two antagonist forces, which act in opposition while they act on, and share between them the subject of the combination in proportion to the intensity of their action; which intensity depends on the quantity of the substance, and on the energy of the affinity: so that the effect increases or diminishes according as the quantity increases or diminishes. It has been already remarked that the absolute weight of any body, multiplied by the degree of its affinity, constitutes its mass.

"It follows as a consequence of the preceding observations, that the action of a substance which tends to decompose a combination, diminishes in proportion as its saturation advances; for this substance may, in such case, be considered as composed of two parts, one of which is saturated, and the other free. The former may be considered as inert, and as unconnected with the latter, the quantity of which diminishes according as the saturation advances; whilst, on the contrary, the action of that which has been eliminated, increases in proportion to the augmentation of its quantity, until the equilibrium of the contending forces ends the operation, and limits the effect."[15]   ▲

Berthollet's studies led to the realization that the course of a chemical reaction is dependent upon a variety of factors, and, consequently, chemical reactions could be effected by factors which were not related to the force of attraction between reacting species. The factors that affect the course of a reaction were enumerated by BERTHOLLET.

▼   "I have considered all the forces which can, by their concurrence with, or opposition to, the reciprocal affinity of substances acting according to the preceding principle, exert any influence on chemical combinations and phenomena. They are reducible to the following: the action of solvents; or the affinity which they exert in proportion to their quantity; the force

[15] *Ibid.,* p. 197.

of cohesion, which is the effect of the mutual affinity of the parts of a simple or compound substance; elasticity, whether natural or produced by caloric,[16] which ought to be considered as an effect of the affinity of caloric; efflorescence, which may be attributed to an affinity not yet determined, acts only in very rare circumstances; gravitation too exerts some influence, particularly when it produces the compression of elastic fluids; but no inconvenience can result from its being confounded with the force of cohesion."[17]

▲

In addition, BERTHOLLET pointed out the error in using Bergman's "elective affinity" to measure the force of interaction between reacting species.

▼   "I have endeavoured to find if it were possible to ascertain the relative affinity of two substances by means of a third; and I have observed that, in order to do so, it would be necessary to ascertain in what proportion that third substance would combine with a given quantity of the two former, or rather in what degree they should participate of its action. I have pointed out the insurmountable obstacles which preclude us from ascertaining and determining this participation of action, and the changes of constitution which may follow.

"As all tables of affinity have been formed on the supposition, that substances are endued with different degrees of affinity, from which originate all the combinations and decompositions that take place, independently of proportion and other circumstances which influence the results, they must give an erroneous idea of the degrees of the chemical action of substances.

"The very term, *elective affinity* must lead into error, as it supposes the union of the whole of one substance with another, in preference to a third; whereas there is only a partition of action, which is itself subordinate to other chemical circumstances."[18]

▲

Berthollet thus clarified the basis for Bergman's affinity tables which were now reduced to lists of chemical reactions. Although the tables could not be used for the purpose they were originally intended, they did provide a means for summarizing and organizing a large body of experimental observations. Bergman and Berthollet did not have the chemical knowledge at their disposal to permit them to discuss the forces which hold molecules together. True, the atomic theory of Democritus had been revived, but the chemists of this period did not know the number of atoms which combined to form, for example, a molecule of water, let alone the electrical constitution of

---

[16] Heat. At this time heat was thought to be a material substance.
[17] *Source Book,* p. 198.
[18] *Ibid.*

atoms. The laws of chemical combination would be enunciated, the concept of valence developed, the ideas of stereochemistry evolved, and the relationship between periodicity and electronic structure realized before the chemical bond would be defined. Hence, BERTHOLLET was forced to reiterate the older gravitational hypothesis in discussing the forces which hold molecules together.

▼   "The powers which produce chemical phenomena are all derived from the mutual attractions of the molecules of the bodies and have been given the name *affinity,* to distinguish them from astronomical attraction.

"It is probable that each is only the same property; but astronomical attraction is exercised only between masses placed at a distance, where the form of the molecules, their intervals, and their particular affections have no influence; its effects, always proportional to the mass and to the inverse of the square of the distance, can be rigorously submitted to calculation: the effects of chemical attraction, or affinity, are on the contrary so altered by the particular conditions, often determinate, that a general principle cannot be deduced; but that it is necessary to establish them successively. Only some of the effects can be so separated from other phenomena as to give them the precision of calculation.

"Thus then, it is only observations that can establish the chemical properties of the bodies, or the affinities by which they exert a reciprocal action in determined conditions; however, since it is very probable that affinity does not differ in its origin from general attraction, it should equally be subject to the laws which mechanics has determined for the phenomena due to the action of mass, and it is natural to think that the more the principles to which the chemical theories apply have generality, the more they have analogy with those of mechanics; but it is only by observation that they can reach that degree which they are already able to indicate."[19]

▲

BERTHOLLET'S ERROR

Unfortunately, the experiments which led Berthollet to clarify Bergman's concepts also led him to propose that the composition of pure substances could be variable. This suggestion, which struck at the heart of what would later develop into the atomic theory, arose from an error in logic rather than from the results of his research. It is ironic that Berthollet's error would impede the development of the atomic hypothesis, which in turn was a necessity for the development of structural concepts. His source of difficulty was the confusion between mixtures and pure substances. It is apparent from his

[19] *Ibid.,* p. 199.

writings that Berthollet considered the solution of a salt in water and chemical combination to be equivalent processes, and this fundamental misunderstanding brought the conclusions he drew into direct conflict with the not too firmly established ideas of the constant composition of pure substances. Proust,[20] on the other hand, more clearly understood the differences between these two interactions as evidenced by the following passage from one of his papers. PROUST queries:

▼   "But what difference, one may say, do you recognize between your chemical combinations and these assemblages of combinations which nature does not bind fast, according to you, in any fixed proportions? Is it that the power which makes a metal dissolve in sulfur is other than that which makes one metallic sulfide dissolve in another?

"I will not hasten to respond to this question, sound as it is, for fear of wandering into a region which the science of facts has perhaps not sufficiently clarified; but one will none the less conceive my distinctions, I hope, when I say, Is the attraction which makes sugar dissolve in water the same or not the same as that which makes a determinate quantity of carbon and hydrogen dissolve in another quantity of oxygen to form the sugar of our plants? But that which we see clearly is that these two sorts of attractions are so different in their results that it is impossible to confound them.

"Thus the solution of niter[21] in water is, for me, not at all like that of azote[22] in oxygen which produces nitric acid or that of nitric acid in potash which produces saltpeter.

"The solution of ammonia in water is to my eyes not at all like that of hydrogen in azote which produces ammonia."[23]   ▲

ESTABLISHMENT OF THE LAW OF CONSTANT COMPOSITION

Proust successfully defended the law of constant proportions in the famous controversy with Berthollet. He showed that the composition of copper carbonate is constant whether it is synthesized in the laboratory or found in nature. From these data PROUST drew the following conclusions.

[20] Joseph Louis Proust (1754–1826): Professor of Chemistry at Salamanca University and later Director of the Royal Laboratory at Madrid. The law of definite composition was established by Proust in the course of an eight-year controversy with Berthollet; the latter believed that chemical combinations could occur to give products with any given proportion of constituents. Proust's work laid the foundation of the law of multiple proportions.

[21] NO_2.

[22] Nitrogen.

[23] J. L. Proust, *Journal de Physique,* **63,** 369 (1806); trans. in *Source Book,* p. 204.

▼   "If 100 parts of this carbonate, dissolved in nitric acid and separated by the alkaline carbonate, gives us 100 parts of artificial carbonate, and if the base of these two combinations is the black oxide, we must recognize that invisible hand which holds the balance for us in the formation of compounds and fashions properties according to its will. We must conclude that nature operates not otherwise in the depths of the world than at its surface or in the hands of man. These ever-invariable proportions, these constant attributes, which characterize true compounds of art or of nature, in a word, this *pondus naturae* so well seen by Stahl; all this, I say, is no more at the power of the chemist than the law of election which presides at all combinations. From these considerations is it not right to believe that the native carbonate of copper will never differ from that which art produces in its imitation? Is there actually any difference between native carbonate of soda and the natural? No. Why, therefore, should there be any difference between those of copper or of other metals when no other perturbing cause has disarranged the reciprocal forces of the factors of these combinations?"[24]   ▲

By the time Proust had demonstrated conclusively to the chemical world that pure substances have a constant composition, Dalton's[25] *A New System of Chemical Philosophy,* which contained his atomic theory, had been published. The ancient ideas concerning the particulate nature of matter had been verified by scientific fact! Avogadro's[26] method for determining relative weights of molecules, and the development of an atomic weight scale by Berzelius,[27] led directly to the method for establishing the formula of

[24] J. L. Proust, *Annales de Chimie, 32,* 26 (1799); trans. in *Source Book,* p. 203.

[25] John Dalton (1766–1844): A Quaker schoolteacher in Manchester, England. His study of gases and their chemical composition led to the formulation of the law of multiple proportions and to an assignment of relative combining weights for the elements. The formulation of the atomic theory and its application to chemical combinations were his greatest contributions to science.

[26] Amadeo Avogadro, Count of Quaregna and of Cerreto (1776–1856): Professor of Physics at the University of Turin. His hypothesis that "equal volumes of gases, measured under the same conditions, contain equal numbers of molecules" was proposed in 1811, but its full meaning and significance were not generally realized until 1860 when it was presented again at a scientific congress by Cannizzaro. Avogadro was the first to distinguish between atoms and molecules.

[27] Jöns Jakob Berzelius (1779–1848): Doctor of Medicine and Professor of Chemistry and Pharmacy in the Karolinschen Medico-Chirurgischen Institut. Berzelius contributed to the dissemination of chemical knowledge by publishing a periodic review (*Jahresbericht*) of new findings which kept him in correspondence with the major chemists of the time. His organizational ability is reflected in his classification of minerals based on chemical properties, his extension and refinement of chemical nomenclature, his introduction of modern symbolism, and his expression of the atomic composition of compounds by formulas. He isolated silicon, titanium, and zirconium, developed a variety of analytical techniques, and established the first scale of atomic weights.

a substance. Previous to the establishment of the concept of molecular formulas, expressed as a combination of atoms in a certain ratio, e.g., NO and NO_2, chemists could describe compounds only in terms of the weight percentage of the elements present, e.g., "the nitrogen oxide containing 46.7% nitrogen and 53.3% oxygen" or "the nitrogen oxide containing 30.4% nitrogen and 69.6% oxygen." It is apparent that any meaningful discussion of the forces which hold nitrogen to oxygen in these compounds was impossible before the concept of molecular structure had been developed. The fact that chemists could show that one oxide of nitrogen had the formula, NO, while another had the formula, NO_2, was an important step in the development of structural concepts since the number of atoms involved in each molecule was known. Questions involving the arrangement of atoms in complex systems could now logically be asked.

ELECTRICITY AND MATTER

About the time that Proust had successfully concluded his defense of the law of constant composition and Dalton had published his atomic theory, Sir Humphry Davy[28] reported the results of his experiments on chemical reactions brought about by electricity. In 1800 Alessandro Volta[29] described an apparatus for the production of electricity which was the forerunner of modern electrochemical cells. Although Volta limited his investigations of electricity to its biological aspects, other chemists, notably Davy and Berzelius, studied the changes which matter underwent under the influence of an electric current. Davy was able to decompose substances by electrolysis which previously had successfully resisted chemical decomposition. In the Bakerian Lecture of 1806, DAVY summarized some of his work on electrolysis which had led him to the following conclusion concerning the nature of the process.

▼   "It will be a general expression of the facts that have been detailed, relating to the changes and transitions by electricity, in common philosophical language, to say, that hydrogene, the alkaline substances, the metals,

[28] Sir Humphry Davy (1778–1829): Professor of Chemistry at the Royal Institution and later President of the Royal Society. Davy, a self-educated chemist with a quick and brilliant mind, was able to recognize and outline new areas of knowledge to be investigated. He applied his talents to practical matters such as agricultural chemistry and the invention of the miner's safety lamp. However, his important contribution to chemistry was the use of electricity to effect chemical reactions. Using this tool, Davy was the first to isolate sodium, potassium, calcium, magnesium, strontium, and barium. In addition, he was the first to demonstrate that chlorine is an elemental substance.

[29] Alessandro Volta (1745–1827): Italian physicist, Professor at Pavia. Although his investigations were mainly in nonchemical areas, e.g., the nature of hail, certain of Volta's electrical researches were significant in the development of chemistry. He constructed the first electric battery ("voltaic pile") which gave chemists a new tool with which to probe into the construction of matter.

and certain metallic oxides, are attracted by negatively electrified metallic surfaces, and repelled by positively electrified metallic surfaces; and contrariwise, that oxygene and acid substances are attracted by positively electrified metallic surfaces, and repelled by negatively electrified metallic surfaces; and these attractive and repulsive forces are sufficiently energetic to destroy or suspend the usual operation of elective affinity.

"It is very natural to suppose, that the repellent and attractive energies are communicated from one *particle to another particle* of the same kind, so as to establish a conducting chain in the fluid; and that the locomotion takes place in consequence; and that this is really the case seems to be shown by many facts. Thus, in all the instances in which I examined alkaline solutions through which acids had been transmitted, I always found acid in them whenever any acid matter remained at the original source. In time, by the attractive power of the positive surface, the decomposition and transfer undoubtedly become complete; but this does not affect the conclusion."[30]   ▲

DAVY suggested not only the existence of charged particles on the basis of his electrolysis experiments, but also that the force of attraction which holds molecules together is electrical in nature.

▼   "As the chemical attraction between two bodies seems to be destroyed by giving one of them an electrical state different from that which it naturally possesses; that is, by bringing it artificially into a state similar to the other, so it may be increased by exalting its natural energy. Thus, whilst zinc, one of the most oxidable of the metals, is incapable of combining with oxygene when negatively electrified in the circuit, even by a feeble power; silver, one of the least oxidable, easily unites to it when positively electrified; and the same thing might be said of other metals.

"Amongst the substances that combine chemically, all those, the electrical energies of which are well known, exhibit opposite states; thus, copper and zinc, gold and quicksilver, sulphur and the metals, the acid and alkaline substances, afford opposite [sic] instances; and supposing perfect freedom of motion in their particles or elementary matter, they ought, according to the principles laid down, to attract each other in consequence of their electrical powers. In the present state of our knowledge, it would be useless to attempt to speculate on the remote cause of the electrical energy, or the reason why different bodies, after being brought into contact, should be found differently electrified; its relation to chemical affinity is, however, sufficiently evident. May it not be identical with it, and an essential property of matter?

[30] H. DAVY, *Philosophical Transactions of the Royal Society of London,* 28 (1807).

"In the present early stage of the investigation, it would be improper to place unbounded confidence in this hypothesis; but it seems naturally to arise from the facts, and to coincide with the laws of affinity, so ably developed by modern chemists; and the general application of it may be easily made.

"Supposing two bodies, the particles of which are in different electrical states, and those states sufficiently exalted to give them an attractive force superior to the power of aggregation, a combination would take place which would be more or less intense according as the energies were more or less perfectly balanced; and the change of properties would be correspondently proportional.

"This would be the simplest case of chemical union. But different substances have different degrees of the same electrical energy in relation to the same body. . . .

"When two bodies repellent of each other act upon the same body with different degrees of the same electrical attracting energy, the combination would be determined by the degree; and the substance possessing the weakest energy would be repelled; and this principle would afford an expression of the causes of elective affinity, and the decompositions produced in consequence.

"Numerical illustrations of these notions might be made without difficulty, and they might be applied to all cases of chemical action; but in the present state of the enquiry, a great extension of this hypothetical part of the subject would be premature.

"The general idea will, however, afford an easy explanation of the influence of affinity by the masses of the acting substances, as elucidated by the experiments of M. Berthollet; for the combined effect of many particles possessing a feeble electrical energy, may be conceived equal or even superior to the effect of a few particles possessing a strong electrical energy."[31]   ▲

BERZELIUS AND THE DUALISTIC THEORY

Davy's suggestions concerning the nature of the forces holding compounds together were supported by Berzelius, who had reached similar conclusions from experiments conducted with William Hisinger. BERZELIUS, however, gave a more detailed description of chemical combination than did Davy.

▼   "In many carefully made experiments, Volta has observed that two metals put in contact become electric, and that this is the cause of the phenomena of the electric pile. Davy later showed that this electrical state

[31] *Ibid.*, p. 39.

increases due to the force of mutual affinities of the bodies used, and that this effect can be produced, and even seen, by means of certain precautions, in all bodies which have affinity for each other. It also follows from the experiments of Davy that temperature, which, as we know, increases affinity, also increases the intensity of the electrical state in bodies which are in contact, but that this mechanical contact being followed by combination, all signs of electricity immediately cease, that is to say, at the instant when, in favorable circumstances, they burst into flame, the electrical division, or the charge which could be perceived, disappears. These facts agree well with the conjecture that the opposite electricities in the bodies which combine, mutually neutralize each other at the moment of combination, and then the fire is produced in the same manner as in the electric discharge.

"But if these bodies, which are united and have ceased to be electric, should again be separated, and their elements restored to the isolated state with their original properties, they must recover the electrical state destroyed by the combination, or indeed, in other terms, if these combined bodies are restored for any reason to their original electrical state, which had vanished at their union, they must separate, and reappear with their original properties. Hisinger and I have observed that when the electric pile exerts its action on a conducting liquid, the elements of this liquid separate, oxygen and the acids are repelled from the negative pole toward the positive, and the combustible bodies as well as the salifiable bases from the positive pole toward the negative.

"We believe we now know with certitude that bodies which are likely to combine show free, opposite electricities which increase in force as they approach the temperature at which combination occurs, until, at the instant of union, the electricity disappears with an elevation of temperature which is often so great that they burst into flame. On the other hand, we have the same certainty that combined bodies exposed in a suitable form to the action of the electric fluid, produced by discharge of a pile, are separated and regain their original chemical and electrical properties at the same time that the electricity which acted on them disappears.

"In the actual state of our knowledge, the most probable explanation of combustion and the ignition which results from it is then: *that in all chemical combinations there is neutralization of opposing electricities, and that this neutralization produces fire in the same manner that it produces it in the discharge of the electric jar, the electric pile, and thunder, without being accompanied, in these latter phenomenon, by chemical combination. . . .*

"The experiments made on the mutual electrical relations of bodies have taught us that they can be divided into two classes: *electropositive* and *electronegative*. The simple bodies which belong to the first class, as well as their oxides, always take up positive electricity when they meet simple bodies or oxides belonging to the second class; and the oxides of the first class always behave with the oxides of the other like salifiable bases with acids."[32]

▲

By suggesting that chemical union occurs because of the neutralization of charges, BERZELIUS was logically led to a consideration of the degree of electrification of various species.

▼   "It has been believed that the electrical series of combustible bodies differs from that of their oxides; but although the different degrees of oxidation of several bodies present exceptions, the electrical order of combustible bodies agrees in general with that of their oxides, in such a way that the strongest degrees of oxidation in the affinity of different radicals are like those between the radicals themselves.

"In arranging the bodies in the order of their electrical nature, there is formed an electro-chemical system which, in my opinion, is more fit than any other to give an idea of chemistry.

"Oxygen is, of all bodies, the most electronegative. As it is never positive relative to any other, and as, according to all chemical phenomena known up to the present it is not probable that any element of our globe can be more electronegative, we recognize in it an absolute negative. Also, in the electrochemical system, it is the only body whose electrical relations are invariable. The others vary in this sense, that one body can be negative with respect to a second, and positive with respect to a third: for example, sulphur and arsenic are positive relative to oxygen and negative relative to metals. The radicals of fixed alkalis and alkaline earths are, on the contrary, the most electropositive bodies; but they differ somewhat in degree; and at the positive extreme of the electrical series, there is no body as electropositive as oxygen is electronegative."[33]

"If these electrochemical views are correct it follows that all chemical combination depends solely on two opposing forces, positive and negative electricity, and that thus each combination should be composed of two parts united by the effect of their electrochemical reaction, provided that there exists no third force. Whence it follows that each compound substance, regardless of the number of its constituent principles, may be divided into two parts, of which one is electrically positive and the other negative."[34]

▲

[32] J. J. BERZELIUS, *Essai sur la Théorie des Proportions Chimiques et sur l'Influence Chimique de l'Électricité* (Paris, 1819), p. 70; trans. in *Source Book*, p. 259.

[33] *Ibid.*, p. 260.

[34] J. J. BERZELIUS, *Larbok i Kemien*, Vol. IV (Paris, 1831); trans. in *Source Book*, p. 261.

Berzelius' description of the chemical bond was essentially correct for ionic substances. We now know that, in the pure state, these substances are composed of a collection of charged particles, all the oppositely charged particles attracting each other, and all the similarly charged particles repelling each other; the stability of a pure crystalline substance suggests that the magnitude of the attractive forces is greater than that of the repulsive forces. Berzelius' theory was successful even when applied to simple molecules that undergo ionization in solution, since we now know that in many instances these molecules are polar; the process of ionization develops a full electronic charge where there existed only a partial charge. A misunderstanding concerning the nature of molecular species and rigid adherence to his electrical concept of combination brought Berzelius' suggestion into direct conflict with the developments in organic chemistry.

Berzelius showed that chlorine was more electronegative than hydrogen, the latter in fact being electropositive. It was thus apparent from the Berzelian point of view that chlorine could never take the place of hydrogen in the formation of compounds. The statement is true if only ionic compounds are considered, but, unfortunately, it does not hold true for the majority of organic compounds, the chemical nature of which would soon be unraveled.

A CRACK IN THE DUALISTIC THEORY

About the time Berzelius was concerned with establishing the dualistic theory of chemical combination, experiments were being conducted by Gay-Lussac[35] which suggested that chlorine could replace hydrogen in hydrocyanic acid (HCN). In his experiments Gay-Lussac obtained proof for the existence of two compounds, hydrogen chloride, HCl, and cyanogen chloride, ClCN, in which chlorine and hydrogen had apparently changed places. Moreover, ClCN (and an equivalent amount of HCl) could be obtained directly from the action of chlorine on HCN, and in a sense Gay-Lussac had described the first substitution reaction.[36] It is apparent from his writing that Gay-Lussac had difficulty in rationalizing the replacement of chlorine by hydrogen in the light of the success of the dualistic theory. At this point he could only state the results of his experiments. Others would develop the concept of substitution reactions, which would eventually lead to the concept of structure.

[35] Joseph Louis Gay-Lussac (1778–1850): Professor at the Paris École Polytechnique. In addition to his studies on the combining volumes of gaseous products and/or reactants, and his investigation into the effect of temperature on the volume of a gas, Gay-Lussac is credited with the isolation of boron. He made the first detailed study of iodine and cyanogen with the aid of Thénard. Among his many important contributions to industry was the "Gay-Lussac tower" used in the manufacturing of sulfuric acid.

[36] It should be noted that ClCN had been prepared earlier by Berthollet.

SUGGESTED READING

Winderlich, R. "Jöns Jakob Berzelius," *Journal of Chemical Education,* **25,** 500 (1948).

CHAPTER 3

Structure

THE ORGANIZATION OF CHEMICAL DATA

Although Berzelius could not explain the problems of chemical combination in organic chemistry by applying his dualistic theory, he contributed indirectly to the ultimate solution of these problems. He introduced the system of chemical symbols which today is used essentially unchanged, as well as a method of writing formulas for compounds in terms of atomic proportions rather than describing them as weight percentages. The basis of BERZELIUS' system is given as follows:

▼ "When we endeavour to express chemical proportions, we find the necessity for chemical signs. Chemistry has always possessed them, though hitherto they have been of very little utility. They owed their origin, no doubt, to the mysterious relation supposed by the alchymists, to exist between the metals and the planets, and to the desire which they had of expressing themselves in a manner incomprehensible to the public. The fellow-laborers in the antiphlogistic revolution published new signs founded on a reasonable principle, the object of which was that the signs, like the new names, should be definitions of the composition of the substances, and that they should be more easily written than the names of the substances themselves. But, though we must acknowledge that these signs were very well contrived, and very ingenious, they were of no use; because it is easier to write an abbreviated word than to draw a figure, which has but little analogy with letters, and which, to be legible, must be made of a larger size than our ordinary writing. In proposing new chemical signs, I shall endeavour to avoid the inconveniences which rendered the old ones of little utility. I must observe here that the object of the new signs is not that, like the old ones, they should be employed to label vessels in the laboratory: they are destined solely to facilitate the expression of chemical proportions, and to enable us to indicate, without long periphrases, the relative number of volumes of the different constituents contained in each compound body. By determining the weight of the elementary volumes, these figures will enable us to express the numeric result of an analysis as simply, and in a manner as easily remembered, as the algebraic formulas in mechanical philosophy.

"The chemical signs ought to be letters, for the greater facility of writing, and not to disfigure a printed book. Though this last circumstance may not appear of any great importance, it ought to be avoided whenever it can be done. I shall take, therefore, for the chemical sign, the *initial letter of the Latin name of each elementary substance:* but as several have the same initial letter, I shall distinguish them in the following manner: 1. In the class which I call *metalloids,* I shall employ the initial letter only, even when this letter is common to the metalloid and some metal. 2. In the class of metals, I shall distinguish those that have the same initials with another metal, or a metalloid, by writing the first two letters of the word. 3. If the first two letters be common to two metals, I shall, in that case, add to the initial letter the first consonant which they have not in common: for example, S = sulphur, Si = silicium, St = stibium (antimony), Sn = stannum (tin), C = carbonicum, Co = cobaltum (cobalt), Cu = cuprum (copper), O = oxygen, Os = osmium, &c.

"The chemical sign expresses always one volume of the substance. When it is necessary to indicate several volumes, it is done by adding the number of volumes: for example, the *oxidum cuprosum* (protoxide of copper) is composed of a volume of oxygen and a volume of metal; therefore its sign is Cu + O. The *oxidum cupricum* (peroxide of copper) is composed of 1 volume of metal and 2 volumes of oxygen; therefore its sign is Cu + 2O. In like manner, the sign for sulphuric acid is S + 3O; for carbonic acid, C + 2O; for water 2H + O, &c.

"When we express a compound volume of the first order, we throw away the +, and place the number of volumes above the letter: for example, $CuO + \overset{3}{SO}$ = sulphate of copper, $\overset{2}{CuO} + 2\overset{3}{SO}$ = persulphate of copper. These formulas have the advantage, that if we take away the oxygen, we see at once the ratio between the combustible radicals. As to the volumes of the second order, it is but rarely of any advantage to express them by formulas as one volume; but if we wish to express them in that way, we may do it by using the parenthesis, as is done in algebraic formulas: for example, alum is composed of 3 volumes of sulphate of aluminia and 1 volume of sulphate of potash. Its symbol is $3(\overset{2}{AlO} + 2\overset{3}{SO}) + (\overset{2}{Po} + 2\overset{3}{SO})$. As to the organic volumes it is at present very uncertain how far figures can be successfully employed to express their composition. We shall have occasion only in the following pages to express the volume of ammonia. It is $6H + N + \overset{6}{O}$ or HNO."[1]   ▲

_____

These innovations provided chemists with a method of organizing analytical data for substances in a manner which facilitated the recognition of significant numerical relationships among series of compounds.

ISOMERISM AND THE CONCEPT OF STRUCTURE

The development of precise analytical techniques led to the realization that certain compounds had the same empirical composition, although they possessed different physical properties and were apparently dissimilar. BERZELIUS, in the 1832 issue of the *Jahresbericht,* the summary of chemical knowledge which he compiled annually, recognized this phenomena and introduced the word "isomer" to the chemist's vocabulary.

_____

▼   "In physical chemistry it was long taken as axiomatic that substances of similar composition, having the same constituents in the same proportions, necessarily must also have the same chemical properties. The investigations of Faraday (*Jahresbericht,* 1827) appear to indicate that there may be an exception to this if two similarly composed substances differ in that the composition of one contains twice as many elementary atoms as occur in the other, although the proportions between the elements remain the same. It is thus with the two gaseous hydrocarbons, olefiant gas,[2] which is $C\overline{H}$,[3] and the other more compressible gas described by Faraday which is $C^2\overline{H}^2$,[4] and accordingly has twice as great a specific gravity as the former. Here, therefore, the similarity in composition is only apparent, for the compound atoms are still definitely different, the relative numbers of elementary atoms being equal but the absolute numbers unequal. Recent researches have now shown that the absolute as well as the relative numbers of elementary atoms may be the same, their combination taking place in such a dissimilar way that the properties of equally composed bodies may be different. We have, however, been led only gradually to such a result. Thus, for instance, I had already demonstrated several years ago that there are two oxides of tin of similar composition,

_____

[1] J. J. BERZELIUS, *Annals of Philosophy,* **3,** 51–52 (1814).
[2] Ethylene (C_2H_4).
[3] A bar through the symbol of an atom represents two atoms.
[4] Butylene (C_4H_8).

but dissimilar properties. Not long afterwards, it was discovered that *Liebig's* fulminic acid and *Wöhler's* cyanic acid have completely identical compositions and saturation capacities. Almost each of the previous volumes of the *Jahresbericht* contains an attempt to discover a possible, hitherto unobserved, dissimilarity in their compositions, without, however, any actually being found. . . .

"Since it is necessary for specific ideas to have definite and consequently as far as possible selected terms, I have proposed to call substances of similar composition and dissimilar properties *isomeric,* from the Greek ισομερης (composed of equal parts). . . ."[5]   ▲

Inherent in the concept of isomerism is the suggestion of a different arrangement of the constituent parts. It should be recalled that some of the ancient Greek philosophers taught that different compound substances were composed of the same atoms but in a different arrangement. In a sense the recognition of the phenomenon of isomerism was a verification of this idea. Indeed, the existence of isomeric substances provided powerful proof of the validity of the atomic theory. These ideas were first alluded to in a paper by GAY-LUSSAC in discussing the difference between cyanic and fulminic acids.

▼   "Thus cyanic acid, according to these data, would be formed by one atom of cyanogen [C_2N_2] and one atom of oxygen; that is to say it is made up of the same constituents and in the same proportions as the acid which Liebig and Gay-Lussac have designated fulminic acid or cyanic acid. But the two acids are very different. The derivatives of one detonate violently when lightly struck, while the others have no such property. To explain these differences it is necessary to postulate a different mode of combination among the elements. This is a matter calling for further examination."[6]   ▲

THE THEORY OF SUBSTITUTION

Although Gay-Lussac had shown earlier that one element could be substituted for another in a simple compound (see page 29), chemists in general

[5] J. J. BERZELIUS, *Jahresbericht über die Fortschritte der Physischen Wissenschaften,* **11,** 44–48 (1832); trans. in *Source Book,* pp. 264–265; see also translation in O. T. Benfey, *From Vital Force to Structural Formulas* (Boston: Houghton Mifflin Company, 1964), p. 27.

[6] J. L. GAY-LUSSAC, *Annales de Chimie et de Physique* [2], **27,** 200 (1824); trans. in O. T. Benfey, *From Vital Force to Structural Formulas* (Boston: Houghton Mifflin Company, 1964), p. 22.

did not appreciate the significance of his results. Wöhler[7] and Liebig,[8] however, presented convincing proof for the replacement of one radical (e.g., a group of atoms that maintain their identity in chemical reactions) by another radical in complex compounds. Their paper entitled "The Researches Concerning the Radical of Benzoic Acid" is a model of clarity and logic. After describing the isolation of benzaldehyde from the "oil of bitter almonds," Wöhler and Liebig showed how this substance can be converted into an alcohol (benzyl alcohol), an acid (benzoic acid), acid halides (benzoyl chloride, benzoyl bromide, benzoyl iodide), an acid amide (benzamide), and an ester (ethyl benzoate). The analyses of the compounds formed in this series of reactions suggested that a part of each of the compounds studied remained unchanged. This idea is expressed in their own words.

▼   "After the determining of this point, and a reviewing of the combining relations of bitter almond oil yet to be considered, we believe it naturally follows that this oil is in its pure state a hydrogen compound, wherein the radical of benzoic acid is combined with 2 atoms of hydrogen, instead of with oxygen as in the acid. This radical as yet unobtained insulated, is composed of $C^{14}H^{10}O^2$. We call it *benzöyl*. The consequent name for the pure oil of bitter almonds is *hydrobenzöyl* (hydroguret of benzöyl,) and for the benzoic acid, *benzöylic acid,* (benzöyl acid). We will however use the common names benzoic acid and bitter almond oil, except in theoretical demonstrations. We will see how easily the remaining relations, to which we now come, will be perceived and comprehended."[9]

"Reviewing and collecting together the relations described in the present essay, we find that they all group around one single compound, which does not change its nature and composition in all its combining relations with other bodies. This stability, this consequence of the phenomena, induced us to consider that body as a compound base and therefore to propose for it a peculiar name, i.e., benzöyl.

"The composition of this radical we have expressed by the formula $14C + 10H + 2O$.

[7] Friedrich Wöhler (1800–1882): Professor at Göttingen. Wöhler's distinguished contributions to chemistry include the transformation of the salt, ammonium cyanate (NH_4OCN), into urea [$(NH_2)_2CO$] which showed conclusively that a "vital force" was not necessary for the formation of organic compounds; the discovery (with Liebig) of the benzoyl radical; and the isolation of aluminum, beryllium, and titanium.

[8] Justus Liebig (1803–1873): Professor at Giessen (1824) and Munich (1852). In addition to his study of the benzoyl radical with Wöhler, which eventually led to the "theory of radicals," Liebig's laboratory became famous for the thorough instruction in experimental chemistry which could be obtained there. He contributed to all areas of chemistry, but especially to agricultural and analytical chemistry.

[9] F. WÖHLER and J. LIEBIG, *Annalen der Pharmacie,* **3,** 240 (1832); trans. by J. C. Booth in *American Journal of Science and Arts,* **26,** 270 (1834).

"In combination with one atom of oxygen, benzöyl forms dry benzoic acid, and in combination with one atom of oxygen, one of water, the crystallized acid.

"In combination with two atoms of hydrogen, it constitutes pure bitter almond oil. When this oil changes in the air into Benzoic acid, it takes up two atoms of oxygen, one of which with the radical generates benzoic acid and the other with the two atoms of hydrogen forms the water of the crystallized acid.

"Farther, the hydrogen of the oil or the oxygen of the acid may be replaced by chlorine, bromine, iodine, sulphur or cyanogen, and the bodies proceeding thence, comparable with the corresponding compounds of phosphorus, all form, by their decomposition with water, on the one side a hydracid, and on the other benzoic acid.

"The replacement, of two atoms of hydrogen in the bitter almond oil by an acidifying base, appears to us in all cases a strong argument for adopting the opinion, that this hydrogen is in a peculiar manner combined with the other elements; this peculiar method of combination may be hinted at rather than pointed out by the idea of the radical, which is borrowed from inorganic chemistry."[10]   ▲

As more information was collected concerning the reactions of organic compounds, the Berzelian concept of duality and its consequences gave way to the Laurent[11] theory of substitution, i.e., that certain radicals in a compound could be replaced by others using relatively simple processes. LAURENT summarized his theory in the following words:

▼   "We have seen that fluorine, chlorine, bromine, and iodine, are the equivalents one of another, and we have refused to admit an equivalence between these bodies and oxygen. We now proceed to inquire, whether among the other simple bodies, there are any which should be associated with them.

"When we cast a general glance at the metamorphosis produced by chlorine, in its action upon organic substances, we perceive the greatest variety.

"Here, for example, are bodies which absorb 2, 4, or 6 atoms of chlorine without any loss; there, on the other hand, are bodies which lose hydrogen

---

[10] *Ibid.,* p. 281.
[11] Auguste Laurent (1807–1853): Professor at Bordeaux. With Gerhardt, he developed a systematic classification for organic compounds which led to the demise of the dualistic theory. Among his accomplishments were the recognition of the distinction between molecular weights, equivalent weights, and atomic weights, and the discovery of anthracene, anthraquinone, and phthalic acid.

without any absorption of chlorine. Here are substances which lose successively 1, 2, 3, 4 . . . atoms of hydrogen, and acquire precisely the same number of atoms of chlorine; there are substances which having lost hydrogen, acquire sometimes more, sometimes less, than an equivalent proportion of chlorine."[12]   ▲

It is apparent that Laurent not only recognized that substitution could occur, but also that some compounds, e.g., ethylene, could react with chlorine without the replacement of hydrogen. In other words, certain hydrocarbons could add chlorine and remain chemically "unsaturated."

▼   "We may remark, that by treating the halydes with chlorine, the majority of them become transformed into hyperhalydes. But as these latter, by the influence of potash, become reconverted into halydes, it is clear that we can obtain the two series of halydes and hyperhalydes, from the same hydrocarbon, by treating it successively with chlorine and potash.

"I take as an example etherine,[13] the reactions of which, when submitted to this alternate treatment, I had pre-indicated. It is to Regnault that we owe the experimental confirmation of what I had advanced. [Read the following as if they were continuous lines.]

	treated by chlorine		which treated by KHO
C^2H^4	produces	C^2H^4. Cl^2	produces
C^2H^3Cl	"	C^2H^3Cl. Cl^2	"
$C^2H^2Cl^2$	"	$C^2H^2Cl^2.Cl^2$	"
C^2H Cl^3	"	C^2H $Cl^3.Cl^2$	"
C^2 Cl^4	"	C^2 $Cl^4.Cl^2$	

"All hydrocarbons do not give rise to hyperhalydes.[14] Turpentine and some others, lose hydrogen only by an equivalent substitution. The halydes formed in this manner, are equally unattackable by potash.

"*Action of Chlorine upon the Hyperhydrides.*[15] The hyperhydrides are to the normal hydrocarbons,[16] what the hyperhalydes are to the halydes. Thus there exists a compound of hydrogen and carbon, which may be represented as etherine *plus* hydrogen, $C^2H^4.H^2$, precisely as Dutch liquid is represented by this same etherine *plus* chlorine, $C^2H^4.Cl^2$.

[12] A. LAURENT, *Chemical Method, Notation, Classification, and Nomenclature;* trans. by W. Odling (London: The Cavendish Society, 1855), p. 184.

[13] Ethylene (C_2H_4).

[14] Hyperhalydes are formed from compounds that absorb chlorine without hydrogen replacement.

[15] Hyperhydrides are the fully saturated hydrocarbons, also called alkanes.

[16] The olefins, e.g., ethylene, were called normal hydrocarbons.

"Let us see in what manner chlorine comports itself with the hyper-hydrides; for example, with the hydruret of etherine.[17]

$$
\begin{aligned}
C^2H^6 \quad &+ Cl^2 \text{ gives rise to } C^2H^5Cl \; + HCl \text{ which is set free.}\\
C^2H^5Cl \; &+ Cl^2 \qquad " \qquad C^2H^4Cl^2 + HCl \qquad\qquad "\\
C^2H^4Cl^2 + Cl^2 \qquad &" \qquad C^2H^3Cl^3 + HCl \qquad\qquad "\\
C^2H^3Cl^3 + Cl^2 \qquad &" \qquad C^2H^2Cl^4 + HCl \qquad\qquad "\\
C^2H^2Cl^4 + Cl^2 \qquad &" \qquad C^2H \; Cl^5 + HCl \qquad\qquad "\\
C^2H \; Cl^5 + Cl^2 \qquad &" \qquad C^2 \quad Cl^6 + HCl \qquad\qquad "
\end{aligned}
$$

Thus, from the first to the last term, there is an equivalent substitution. We have compared the hyperhydrides to the hyperhalydes; this comparison is warranted by the action of potash upon their *derivatives,* which are thereby converted into halydes.[18]

"I call a chloro-compound a *derivative* of some other body, when its composition may be represented by that of the other body, *minus* hydro-gen, *plus* an *equivalent* quantity of chlorine. Thus C^2H^5Cl is a derivative of C^2H^6, — C^2Cl^4 is a derivative of C^2H^4, and chloride of benzoyl, C^7H^5ClO, is a derivative of oil of bitter almonds, C^7H^6O. Since I first made use of this term, other chemists have employed it, but in another and very loose signification. Thus, according to them, Dutch liquid is a derivative of etherine, picric acid a derivative of indigo, &c. I retain the signification which I originally gave to the term, and thus when I say, that trichloroacetic acid is a derivative of acetic acid, I mean, that this latter has lost three equivalents of hydrogen, and gained three equivalents of chlorine.

"I ought not to close this subject without remarking, that marsh gas $CH^2.H^2$, the most simple of all the hyperhydrides, appears to comport it-self differently from the rest of them. By the action of chlorine, it gives rise to the following derivatives: CH^3Cl, CH^2Cl^2, $CHCl^3$, CCl^4; these, like the ordinary hyperhalydes, are decomposed by potash, but, in a different manner. Thus the compound $CHCl^3$ would be chloroform, and would consequently yield, by the action of potash, formic acid, CH^2O^2, instead of chloride of carbon, CCl^2; the compound CH^3Cl would be the chloride of methyl, and when acted upon by potash would give rise to methylic alco-hol. Nevertheless I ought to remark, that the experiments made upon this subject require to be repeated."[19]   ▲

Thus, one of the "principles" underlying Berzelius' theory of dualism had been overpowered by the weight experiment; the results of other experiments

[17] Hydruret of etherine is ethane.
[18] Halydes are the products formed when chlorine replaces hydrogen in a compound.
[19] A. LAURENT, *op. cit.,* pp. 187–190.

brought down what remained of the attempt to apply the dualistic theory to covalent compounds. In the dualistic scheme, as applied to inorganic compounds, the replacement of an electronegative element by an electropositive element in an oxide usually changed the oxide from a base to an acid, e.g., Na_2O and P_2O_3. Dumas[20] substituted three of the hydrogen atoms in acetic acid by chlorine to form trichloroacetic acid, but this substitution of the electronegative element chlorine for the electropositive element hydrogen produced a substance which was still acidic! DUMAS described trichloroacetic acid as:

▼   ". . . chlorinated vinegar, but what is very remarkable, at least for those who refuse to find in chlorine a body capable of replacing hydrogen in the precise and complete sense of the word, this chlorinated vinegar is just as much an acid as common vinegar itself. Its acid power is not changed. It saturates the same quantity of alkali as before, and saturates it equally well, and the salts to which it gives rise exhibit, when compared with acetates, resemblances full of interest and generality.

"Here then is a new organic acid, containing a very considerable quantity of chlorine, and exhibiting none of the reactions of chlorine; its hydrogen has disappeared, and has been replaced by chlorine, and yet this remarkable substitution has produced only a slight change in its properties, all its essential characters remaining unaltered. . . ."[21]   ▲

CHEMICAL TYPES

Dumas developed the substitution theory into a theory of chemical types in which organic compounds were classified on the basis of their chemical properties in much the same manner as were inorganic compounds. Thus, trichloroacetic acid, acetic acid, and benzoic acid are all of the acid type. DUMAS' development of the type theory follows.

▼   "What has been found in inorganic nature to be a useful and a true guide, isomorphism, is a theory which, as is well known, rests on facts, and which, as is equally well known, is little in accordance with the electrochemical theory.

[20] Jean Baptiste André Dumas (1800–1884): Professor of Chemistry at the Sorbonne. Dumas' skill as an experimentalist is still evident in the methods which carry his name: the determination of nitrogen in organic compounds and the determination of the density of volatile substances. His studies of the reactions of organic compounds with chlorine led to the theory of types and the downfall of the dualistic theory.

[21] J. B. A. DUMAS, *Annalen der Chemie und Pharmacie*, **22**, 101 (1829); trans. in W. A. Shenstone, *Justus von Liebig, His Life and Work* (New York: The Macmillan Company, 1895), pp. 59–60.

"Now in organic chemistry the theory of substitution plays the same part as isomorphism in mineral chemistry; and perhaps we may some day by experience find that these two general points of view are intimately related, being dependent on the same causes and capable of being comprised in a common expression.

"For the present, from the transformation of acetic acid into chloracetic acid, from that of aldehyde into chloral; from the fact that the hydrogen of these bodies is replaced by chlorine, volume for volume, without altering their original nature we must conclude:

"*That there exist in organic chemistry certain TYPES which remain as such, even after replacing their hydrogen by an equal volume of chlorine, bromine or iodine; i.e.* the theory of substitution rests on facts, on the most striking facts of organic chemistry."[22]   ▲

Dumas was, of course, attacked by Berzelius for these suggestions on the grounds that trichloroacetic acid had properties very different from those associated with acetic acid. In a subsequent paper, DUMAS attempted to clarify his suggestion.

▲   "In a memoir which I had the honor of communicating to the Academy some time ago I showed that chlorine decomposes acetic acid under the influence of solar light and that it gives rise to a new acid which I have named chloroacetic acid.

"I expressed on that occasion the opinion that acetic acid and chloroacetic acid belong to the same chemical type, $A^8B^8C^4$, one being represented by $C^8H^8O^4$ and the other by $C^8H^2O^4$,

$$Ch^6.$$

"I have attempted to generalize this point of view and to show how these types may serve to group these organic substances in well-characterized genera.

"As soon as he was acquainted with my memoir, M. Berzelius, who denies the theory of substitutions, published a refutation of the views which I gave there. This illustrious scientist regards acetic and chloracetic acid as very different from one another because they have not the same density, boiling point, nor odor, etc.

"M. Berzelius has certainly not understood what I have called the *fundamental properties* of substances, for long ago I knew that in replacing the hydrogen in a compound by chlorine the compound is rendered more dense and less volatile and that at the same time its vapor density is increased.

[22] *Ibid.,* **32,** 101 (1839); trans. in C. Schorlemmer, *The Rise and Development of Organic Chemistry* (London: The Macmillan Company, 1894), pp. 41–42.

"Moreover, it is perfectly clear to me that the objections advanced by M. Berzelius do not apply at all to the views which I actually intended to express.

"However, to prevent all misunderstanding I will attempt to state my idea precisely by means of an example.

"By treating chloracetic acid with any alkali I have obtained a very remarkable reaction. The acid is converted into two new substances, namely, carbonic acid, which is combined with the alkali, and chloroform, which is liberated. We have thus

$$C^8H^2O^4 = C^4O^4 + C^4H^2$$
$$Ch^6 \qquad\qquad Ch^6.$$

"I was convinced, and I announced it after a fashion in my memoir, that acetic acid would give an analogous reaction: that is to say, that under the influence of an excess of base it would change into carbonic acid and a hydrocarbon which should have C^4H^8 for a formula.

"After several inevitable trials I have completely succeeded in producing this remarkable reaction."[23]   ▲

Thus, chemists began to consider the relationship between compounds in terms of atomic groupings, a necessary prelude to elucidation of their geometric arrangement. Dumas showed that organic compounds consist of units which usually react in the same way irrespective of the fact that hydrogen may have been substituted by another monovalent element. Laurent contributed to Dumas' concept of "types" when he published a table showing the relationships between certain acids, bases, salts, alcohols, and ethers (Table 3–1).

TABLE 3–1*

	Hydrogen acid	Hydrogen sulfide acid	Sulfurous acid	Sulfuric acid	Carbonic acid	Oxalic acid
Acid	OHH	SHH	SO_3HH	SO_4HH	CO_3HH	C_2O_4HH
Acid salt	OHK	SHK	SO_3HK	SO_4HK	CO_3HK	C_2O_4HK
Neutral salt	OKK	SKK	SO_3KK	SO_4KK	CO_3KK	C_2O_4KK
Double salt	OKM	SKM	SO_3KM	SO_4KM	CO_3KM	C_2O_4KM
Salt	OEtK	SEtK	SO_3EtK	SO_4EtK	CO_3EtK	C_2O_4EtK
Ether	OEtEt	SEtEt	SO_3EtEt	SO_4EtEt	CO_3EtEt	C_2O_4EtEt

* Reprinted from Auguste Laurent, *Annales de Chimie et de Physique* [3], **78**, 293 (1846).

[23] J. B. A. DUMAS, *Comptes Rendus,* **9**, 813–815 (1839); trans. in *Source Book,* p. 327.

It is apparent from Table 3–1 that Laurent recognized the formalism which exists between, for example, H_2O, KOH, C_2H_5OH, and $C_2H_5OC_2H_5$, in spite of the marked dissimilarities of these substances. Dumas' "type theory" suggested that organic compounds could be classified according to the substitution of a simple parent compound, e.g., water, by characteristic groups of atoms (radicals). Eventually, the results from many laboratories supported this concept. WILLIAMSON[24] amplified Laurent's "water type" to include both inorganic and organic substances.

▼   "I believe that throughout inorganic chemistry, and for the best-known organic compounds, one single type will be found sufficient; it is that of water, represented as containing 2 atoms of hydrogen to 1 of oxygen, thus $\begin{smallmatrix}H\\H\end{smallmatrix}O$. In many cases a multiple of this formula must be used, and we shall

presently see how we thereby get an explanation of the difference between monobasic and bibasic acids, &c.

"I will here give a few examples of the application of this universal type to the formulae of common substances. The experiments of M. Chancel, agreeing in result with my own, have clearly proved that the numerous family designated as hydrated oxides are not formed by the juxtaposition of an atom of water with an atom of metallic oxide, e.g., $K^2O + H^2O$, but

that the equivalent of the molecule is half of that quantity, namely $\begin{smallmatrix}H\\K\end{smallmatrix}O$;

they are not compounds of water, but products of substitution in water. This fact is as applicable to the compound as to the simple radicals; and alcohols, which are truly hydrated oxides, must be considered as products of substitution of the compound radicals, methyle, CH^3 aethyle, C^2H^5; amyle, C^5H^{11}; oenanthyle, C^7H^{15}; &c. for half the hydrogen of water, $\begin{smallmatrix}H\\(CH^3)\end{smallmatrix}O$, $\begin{smallmatrix}H\\C^2H^5\end{smallmatrix}O$, &c. The anhydrous oxides of metals have both atoms of

hydrogen replaced by the metal, as $\begin{smallmatrix}K\\K\end{smallmatrix}O$, in the same way as common

aether, and its homologues have aethyle in place of both the atoms of hydrogen.

"In extending this mode of notation to salts and compound aethers, we must of course keep carefully in view the capacity of saturation of their acids, writing the monobasic acids as hydrochloric, nitric, acetic, &c. at

---

[24] Alexander William Williamson (1824–1904): Professor of Chemistry at University College, London. In spite of the loss of an arm and the sight of one eye when he was a child, Williamson made many contributions to chemistry. His most significant contribution was the elucidation of the chemical relationship which exists between an alcohol and an ether.

half their usual equivalents, ClH, NO^3 H, C^2 H^4 O^2, but retaining the customary atomic weights of the bibasic acids, as sulphuric, carbonic, oxalic, &c.

"As alcohol is truly an acid in its reaction, we must of course consider the potassium-alcohol, $\begin{matrix} C^2H^5 \\ K \end{matrix}$ O, as its salt, though alkaline in its reaction. We only need to replace 2 atoms of hydrogen in the radical of this salt by oxygen, to have a compound of which the saline character is acknowledged, acetate of potash, $\begin{matrix} (C^2H^3O) \\ K \end{matrix}$ O. The most simple manner of representing the rational constitution of this compound is to state that it contains, in lieu of the aethyle of the former salt, an oxygen-aethyle, C^2H^3O, which we may term othyle. If the 2 atoms of hydrogen in water were replaced by this othyle, we should have anhydrous acetic acid, $\begin{matrix} (C^2H^3O) \\ (C^2H^3O) \end{matrix}$ O. In fact, the so-called anhydrous acids are nothing else than the *aethers* of the hydrated acids.

"Again, by replacing the potassium in the aethylate, $\begin{matrix} C^2H^5 \\ K \end{matrix}$ O, by its equivalent of cyanogen (which may be effected by the action of iodide of cyanogen), we obtain a compound of the composition $\begin{matrix} C^2 H^5 \\ (NC) \end{matrix}$ O, that is, cyanic aether."[25]

"My object in commencing the experiments was to obtain new alcohols by substituting carburetted hydrogen for hydrogen in a known alcohol. With this view I had recourse to an expedient, which may render valuable services on similar occasions. It consisted in replacing the hydrogen first by potassium and acting upon the compound thus formed by the chloride or iodide of the carburetted hydrogen which was to be introduced in the place of that hydrogen. I commenced with common alcohol, which, after careful purification, was saturated with potassium, and as soon as the action had ceased, mixed with a portion of iodide of aethyle equivalent to the potassium used. Iodide of potassium was readily formed on the application of a gentle heat, and the desired substitution was effected; but, to my astonishment, the compound thus formed had none of the properties of an alcohol — it was nothing else than common aether, $C^4H^{10}O$.

"Now this result at once struck me as being inconsistent with the higher formula of alcohol; for if that body contained twice as many atoms of oxygen as are in aether, I ought clearly to have obtained a product con-

25 A. W. WILLIAMSON, *Journal of the Chemical Society,* **4,** 350 (1852); printed earlier in the *Chemical Gazette,* **9,** 334 (1851).

taining twice as much oxygen as aether does. The alternative was evident; for having obtained aether by substituting C^2H^5 for H in alcohol, the relative composition of the two bodies is represented *by expressing that fact in our formula.* Thus alcohol is $\begin{smallmatrix} C^2H^5 \\ H \end{smallmatrix} O$, and the potassium compound is $\begin{smallmatrix} C^2H^5 \\ K \end{smallmatrix} O$; and by acting upon this by iodide of aethyle, we have

$$\begin{smallmatrix} C^2H^5 \\ K \end{smallmatrix} O \; + \; C^2H^5I \; = \; IK \; + \; \begin{smallmatrix} C^2H^5 \\ C^2H^5 \end{smallmatrix} O.$$

"Of course the proportion between the two bodies is the only point upon which I here enter, and the same reasoning would be applicable to any multiple of the formulae assumed. Some chemists may perhaps prefer doubling them in order to avoid the use of atoms of hydrogen, potassium, &c.; but I have not felt myself justified in doing so, because that would involve doubling the usual formula for water; for, as I will presently show, water is formed in aetherification by replacing the carburetted hydrogen of alcohol by hydrogen, which, of course, obliges us to assume the same unity of oxygen in both. Alcohol is therefore water in which half the hydrogen is replaced by carburetted hydrogen, and aether is water in which both atoms of hydrogen are replaced by carburetted hydrogen: thus,[26]

$$\begin{smallmatrix} H \\ H \end{smallmatrix} O, \quad \begin{smallmatrix} C^2H^5 \\ H \end{smallmatrix} O, \quad \begin{smallmatrix} C^2H^5 \\ C^2H^5 \end{smallmatrix} O."$$

▲

The "type theory," as expounded by Laurent and Williamson, was perhaps most concisely summarized by Gerhardt.[27] In his systematic treatise of 1853, GERHARDT wrote:

▼   "To arrange organic compounds in series, that is, to determine the laws according to which the properties in a given type are modified by substitution of an element or group of elements for other elements, this is the constant purpose of the chemist philosopher. These thousands of compounds which he produces in his laboratory are for him, however, the terms which serve him to construct his series. Today, in the imperfect state of the science, there is still need for many terms; but later, knowledge of certain series will eliminate direct study of many other terms whose

[26] A. W. WILLIAMSON, *Philosophical Magazine,* **37,** 350 (1850).
[27] Charles Frederic Gerhardt (1816–1856): Professor of Chemistry at Montpellier and Strasbourg. A student of Liebig, Gerhardt and his work are closely associated with that of Laurent. Gerhardt proposed that all organic compounds could be related to the inorganic compounds, water, hydrogen chloride, hydrogen, and ammonia. He discovered quinoline and the acid chlorides and acid anhydrides of monobasic organic acids.

properties he will be able to predict with the same certainty as he predicts today the properties of propionic or valeric alcohols, even though he has not yet obtained these alcohols.

"In the state of the science, organic compounds can be related to three or four types, each capable of giving series which resemble those represented by formic and stearic acids, potash, and sulfuric acids; these types are

Water	H^2O
Hydrogen	H^2
Hydrochloric acid	HCl
Ammonia	H^3N

By exchanging their hydrogens among certain groups, these types give rise to acids, to alcohols, to ethers, to hydrides, to radicals, to organic chlorides, to acetones, to alkalis.

"The series formed by each type has its extremes, which can be called the positive, or left, side and the negative, or right, side. An organic group, substituting for hydrogen, which places itself on the positive side will produce compounds placed on the same side; the groups ethyl CH^3 (sic), methyl C^2H^3 (sic), amyl C^5H^{11}, for example, will give by this substitution alcohols resembling water, aldehydes or radicals resembling hydrogen, ethers resembling hydrochloric acid, alkalis resembling ammonia. The groups of which I speak resemble, in fact, potash or other reputedly electropositive metals; the oxides (the alcohols) and the alkalis to which they give rise behave like bases, in that they can combine with acids placed at the other extreme of the series.

"Other organic groups, for example cyanogen CN, acetyl C^2H^3O, benzoyl C^7H^5O, on substituting for the hydrogen of the types mentioned give rise to those compounds which are farther removed than the preceding from compounds formed with hydrogen, to compounds which are placed more to the right, toward the negative extreme. The oxides formed by these groups resemble sulfuric acid more than potash. . . .

"The *water* type, changing half its hydrogen for a hydrocarbon group CH^3, C^2H^5, etc., gives rise to an alcohol; changing all its hydrogen for a similar group, it produces the corresponding ether.

"The same type, in changing half its hydrogen for a group containing at once carbon, hydrogen, and oxygen, produces a hydrated monobasic acid, resembling acetic acid. When the substitution is effected by the same group on the two atoms of hydrogen of water, the product is the corresponding acid anhydride; Mr. Williamson has already made the same comparison, and its exactitude seems to me today to be perfectly demonstrated by my experiments. Finally, when the substitution of the two hydrogen atoms of water is made half by a hydrocarbon group like ethyl or methyl and half by an oxygenated group resembling that which is found in a monobasic acid, the ester of this acid is obtained.

"The *hydrogen* type can undergo the same substitutions as the water type and produce as many combinations.

"The compounds resembling marsh gas, known as *hydrides,* are evidently related to hydrogen as alcohols are to water; the ethyl and methyl radicals correspond to the ethers of these alcohols. Aldehydes are to hydrogen as monobasic acids are to water; acetyl, benzoyl, and other oxygenated radicals correspond to acid anhydrides; the acetones, finally, as M. Chancel has already remarked, represent the esters of the aldehydes and consequently are to hydrogen as the esters of monobasic acids are to water.

"The *hydrochloric acid* type gives rise, on the one hand, to hydrochloric ethers, that is, to chlorides resembling chloride of potassium or chlorides of electropositive elements, when the substitution is effected by hydrocarbon groups; and, on the other hand, to electronegative chlorides corresponding to monobasic acids, like acetyl chloride or benzoyl chloride, when the same substitution is effected by groups contained in these monobasic acids.

"Finally, the *ammonia* type produces alkalis able to combine with acids, or amides able to combine with bases (oxide of silver, mercury, copper, etc.), according to whether the substitution on the hydrogens of the ammonia is effected by groups which give rise to bases (alcohols, organic oxides), or by groups which produce organic acids. The bodies resembling the hydrate of oxide of ammonia are represented at the other end of the series by acid amides.

"It can be seen by this rapid summary how the application of the notion of series permits simplification of the general theory of organic compounds. They no longer terrify by their number and variety, for, instead of being formulated by special theories which lack any connection, as they are called ethers, amides, alkalis, or acids, they become simply terms whose properties can be predicted according to the place they occupy in the series. And what certainly adds to the advantage of such a system is the similarity of method of formation or decomposition which it expresses for all the bodies which it contains. Experiment shows, in fact, that organic compounds are almost all the result of *double decompositions* resembling those which we effect in mineral chemistry."[28]   ▲

To emphasize the individuality of radicals in various compounds, chemists began to employ formulas in which the positions of the reacting radicals on the printed page were important (cf. Williamson's discussion of the "water

[28] C. GERHARDT, *Annales de Chimie et de Physique,* **37,** 336 (1853); trans. in *Source Book,* p. 351.

type" on page 42). The significance of this type of symbolism was apparent to WILLIAMSON when he wrote:

▼   "The chemical formulae, by which we describe more briefly than by words the transformations supposed known to take place, have as yet answered that purpose very imperfectly, and have presented great irregularity of method; for although generally denoting a certain arrangement of atoms, or at least certain differences of arrangement, they are sometimes used to describe the origin of a compound or its decompositions, without forming any other representation of its actual constitution than what may be contained in such a statement. M. Gerhardt has, in a recent memoir published conjointly with M. Chancel, given considerable development to this latter method; and his so-called synoptic formulae will, I think, be found very suggestive and useful expressions. But formulae may be used in an entirely different, and yet perfectly definite manner, and the use of two distinct points of view will perhaps not be unserviceable. They may be used as an actual image of what we rationally suppose to be the arrangement of constituent atoms in a compound, as an orrery is an image of what we conclude to be the arrangement of our planetary system; and decompositions may be actually effected between them by the exchange of a molecule in one group for a molecule in another. Gerhardt's formula for sulphate of soda (if he extends his principles to inorganic chemistry) would be sulphuric acid plus soda minus water. This, no doubt, gives a possible origin of the salt, but by no means a possible decomposition; in other instances the inverse would be the case. But the term sulphate of soda does not mean a body formed in any one particular way; it is equally applicable to the product of the action of sulphuric acid on chloride of sodium, or on carbonate of soda, or even to the product of the action of soda on sulphate of iron. The written name should be made to represent what we conceive a compound *to be,* and should be such that it might be formed by any one of the various processes by which the compound may be prepared. Sulphate of soda is a physical term, and corresponds to purely physical properties; for the substance described by it does not by itself undergo any change, but only when acted upon by certain foreign substances under suitable circumstances.

"When we study a molecule by itself, we study it physically; chemistry considers the *change* effected by its reaction upon another molecule, and has to describe the process by which that change is effected. A chemical decomposition should therefore be represented by the juxtaposition of the formulae of the reacting substances, and by effecting in these formulae the change which takes place in the mixture."[29]   ▲

29 A. W. WILLIAMSON, *Chemical Gazette,* **9,** 334 (1851); reprinted in *Papers on Etherification and on the Constitution of Salts,* Alembic Club Reprint, No. 16 (Edinburgh: Oliver and Boyd, 1923), p. 42.

WILLIAMSON, in fact, attempted to use this type of symbolism to describe the reaction between sodium ethoxide (EtONa) and ethyl iodide to form ether.

▼   "The reaction is easily understood by the following diagram, in which the atoms

are supposed to be capable of changing places by turning round upon the central point A.

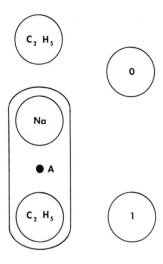

"It is clear that we thus get $\begin{matrix} C_2H_5 \\ C_2H_5 \end{matrix}O$ and NaI. The circles are merely used to separate off the atoms or units of comparison. To express the corresponding decomposition of iodide of ethyle by hydrate of potash, forming alcohol, we should replace the ethyle of the sodium-compound by hydrogen, and the same change of place between sodium and ethyle forms $\begin{matrix} H \\ C_2H_5 \end{matrix}O$ (alcohol) and NaI."[30]   ▲

---

[30] A. W. WILLIAMSON, *Journal of the Chemical Society*, **4**, 229 (1852); reprinted in *Papers on Etherification and on the Constitution of Salts*, Alembic Club Reprint, No. 16 (Edinburgh: Oliver and Boyd, 1923), p. 28.

THE CONCEPT OF VALENCE

Two steps were to follow before a consideration of geometrical factors would arise naturally. First, the concept of valence had to be established, and, second, the concept of a bond holding the units of a molecule together was necessary. To Frankland[31] goes the credit of explicitly stating that compounds of the elements exhibit a regularity concerning the number of radicals to which they can be attached, although this concept was implicit in the formulas which Williamson and Gerhardt presented to describe the "type theory." In his report on the formation of compounds containing organic radicals, FRANKLAND discoursed on the subject of valence.

▼   "Taking this view of the so-called conjugate organic radicals, and regarding the oxygen, sulphur or chlorine compounds of each metal as the true molecular type of the organo-metallic bodies derived from it by the substitution of an organic group for oxygen, sulphur, &c., . . . we have the . . . inorganic types and organo-metallic derivatives [see page 50].

"When the formulae of inorganic chemical compounds are considered, even a superficial observer is struck with the general symmetry of their construction; the compounds of nitrogen, phosphorus, antimony and arsenic especially exhibit the tendency of these elements to form compounds containing 3 or 5 equivs. of other elements and it is in these proportions that their affinities are best satisfied; thus in the ternal group we have NO_3, NH_3, NI_3, NS_3, PO_3, PH_3, PCl_3, SbO_3, SbH_3, $SbCl_3$, AsO_3, AsH_3, $AsCl_3$, &c; and in the five-atom group NO_5, NH_4O, NH_4I, PO_5, PH_4I, &c. Without offering any hypothesis regarding the cause of this symmetrical grouping of atoms, it is sufficiently evident, from the examples just given, that such a tendency or law prevails, and that, no matter what the character of the uniting atoms may be, the combining power of the attracting element, if I may be allowed the term, is always satisfied by the same number of these atoms. It was probably a glimpse of the operation of this law amongst the more complex organic groups, which led Laurent and Dumas to the enunciation of the theory of types; and had not those distinguished chemists extended their views beyond the point to which they were well supported by then existing facts — had they not assumed, that the properties of an organic compound are dependent upon the position and not upon the nature of its single atoms, that theory would undoubtedly have contributed to the development of the science to a still greater extent than it has already done; such an assumption could only have been

[31] Sir Edward Frankland (1825–1899): Professor at the Royal Institution (1863) and the Royal College (1865). Frankland was a pupil of Bunsen and Kolbe. His research in the field of organometallic chemistry led to a clear statement of the valence concept. He was associated with Lockyer in the discovery of helium in the sun.

Inorganic Types.   Organo-metallic Derivatives.

$$As\begin{Bmatrix} S \\ S \end{Bmatrix} \quad . \quad . \quad As\begin{Bmatrix} C_2H_3 \\ C_2H_3 \end{Bmatrix} Cacodyl.$$

$$As\begin{Bmatrix} O \\ O \\ O \end{Bmatrix} \quad . \quad . \quad As\begin{Bmatrix} C_2H_3 \\ C_2H_3 \\ O \end{Bmatrix} Oxide\ of\ Cacodyl.$$

$$As\begin{Bmatrix} O \\ O \\ O \\ O \\ O \end{Bmatrix} \quad . \quad . \quad As\begin{Bmatrix} C_2H_3 \\ C_2H_3 \\ O \\ O \\ O \end{Bmatrix} Cacodylic\ acid.$$

$$Zn \quad O \quad . \quad . \quad Zn\ (C_2H_3)\ Zincmethylium.$$

$$Zn\begin{Bmatrix} O \\ O_x \end{Bmatrix} \quad . \quad . \quad Zn\begin{Bmatrix} C_2H_3 \\ O_x \end{Bmatrix} Oxide\ of\ Zincmethylium.$$

$$Sb\begin{Bmatrix} O \\ O \\ O \end{Bmatrix} \quad . \quad . \quad Sb\begin{Bmatrix} C_4H_5 \\ C_4H_5 \\ C_4H_5 \end{Bmatrix} Stibethine.$$

$$Sb\begin{Bmatrix} O \\ O \\ O \\ O \\ O \end{Bmatrix} \quad . \quad . \quad Sb\begin{Bmatrix} C_4H_5 \\ C_4H_5 \\ C_4H_5 \\ O \\ O \end{Bmatrix} Binoxide\ of\ Stibethine.$$

$$Sb\begin{Bmatrix} O \\ O \\ O \\ O \\ O \end{Bmatrix} \quad . \quad . \quad Sb\begin{Bmatrix} C_4H_5 \\ C_4H_5 \\ C_4H_5 \\ C_4H_5 \\ O \end{Bmatrix} Oxide\ of\ Stibethylium.$$

$$Sn \quad O \quad . \quad . \quad Sn\ (C_4H_5)\ Stanethylium.$$

$$Sn\begin{Bmatrix} O \\ O \end{Bmatrix} \quad . \quad . \quad Sn\begin{Bmatrix} C_4H_5 \\ O \end{Bmatrix} Oxide\ of\ Stanethylium.$$

$$Hg\begin{Bmatrix} I \\ I \end{Bmatrix} \quad . \quad . \quad Hg\begin{Bmatrix} C_2H_3 \\ I \end{Bmatrix} \begin{matrix} Iodide\ of \\ Hydrargyromethylium. \end{matrix}$$

made at a time when the data upon which it was founded were few and imperfect, and, as the study of the phenomena of substitution progressed, it gradually became untenable, and the fundamental principles of the electro-chemical theory again assumed their sway. The formation and examination of the organo-metallic bodies promise to assist in effecting a fusion of the two theories which have so long divided the opinions of chemists, and which have too hastily been considered irreconcileable; for, whilst it is evident that certain types of series of compounds exist, it is equally clear that the nature of the body derived from the original type is essentially dependent upon the electro-chemical character of its single atoms, and not merely upon the relative position of those atoms."[32]   ▲

Structural Formulas

Chemists had now explicitly developed the concept of valence, i.e., combining power. This meant, for example, that an oxygen atom was always attached to two other radicals or atoms, as in H_2O, Et_2O, and $EtOH$. Other elements such as nitrogen could exhibit variable valences, but within certain groups of compounds containing these atoms, a pattern emerged. Thus, nitrogen-containing compounds exhibited a valence of 3 in compounds like NH_3, CH_3NH_2, $(CH_3)_2NH$, and $(CH_3)_3N$. As more complex combinations of radicals were discovered, Williamson's method of describing a compound was extended: Gerhardt[33] proposed the structure, $\left.\begin{array}{l} C_2H_3O \\ H \\ H \end{array}\right\} N$, for acet-

amide,[34] and Kekulé[35] pictured urea[36] as $CO \begin{array}{l} H \\ H \end{array}\Big\} N$. Indeed, Kekulé contributed $\begin{array}{l} H \\ H \end{array}\Big\} N$

markedly to our present concept of a formula when he wrote:

▼   "Rational formulas are reaction formulas . . . . their symbolism indicates the atomic groups that remain unattacked in certain reactions (radicals), or emphasize the constituent parts which play a role in certain often recurring metamorphoses (types), they are intended to provide a picture of the chemical nature of a substance. Every formula, therefore, that expresses certain metamorphoses of a compound, is *rational;* among the different rational formulas, however, that one is the *most rational* which expresses simultaneously the largest number of metamorphoses.

[32] E. FRANKLAND, *Philosophical Transactions of the Royal Society of London,* **142,** 417 (1852).

[33] C. Gerhardt, *Annales de Chimie et de Physique* [3], **37,** 285 (1853).

[34] The modern structural formula for acetamide is $CH_3—CO—NH_2$.

[35] Friedrich August Kekulé (1829–1896): Professor of Chemistry at Ghent (1858) and Bonn (1867). Kekulé studied under the leading chemists of that age, Dumas, Würtz, Gerhardt, and Liebig. He proposed the tetravalence of carbon, suggested that carbon atoms can join to each other, and extended these ideas to the ring formulation for benzene.

[36] A. KEKULÉ, *Annalen der Chemie und Pharmacie,* **106,** 129 (1858). The modern structural formula for urea is $H_2N—CO—NH_2$.

"Of the three rational formulas of benzenesulfonic acid:

$$\left.\begin{array}{c} \text{—C}_6\text{H}_5 \\ \text{SO}_2 \\ \text{H} \end{array}\right\}\text{—O—} \qquad \left.\begin{array}{c} \text{—C}_6\text{H}_5\text{SO}_2 \\ \\ \text{H} \end{array}\right\}\text{—O—} \qquad \text{—C}_6\text{H}_5\text{SO}_3,\text{H}$$

the first designates (1) that 1 atom H is easily exchanged for metals, (2) that under the action of PCl_5, chlorine takes up the position of the typical —O— and, in addition to HCl, the chloride $C_6H_5SO_2,Cl$ is formed; it designates (3) that benzenesulfonic acid can be formed from a phenyl and a sulfuryl compound; it therefore expresses all known metamorphoses of this acid and brings to recollection its relations to benzene and sulfuric acid. The second formula expresses only metamorphoses (1) and (2), while the third finally (hydrogen acid theory) designates only salt formation and takes no account of any other reactions. The first is, therefore, by far the most comprehensive and therefore the most rational. The advantages from this point of view of writing formulas according to "mixed types" appears most clearly (in addition to the sulfonic acids) in connection with the more complex compounds of nitrogen.

"The formula of an amino acid

$$\begin{array}{c} \text{H} \\ \text{H} \\ \text{—C}_2\text{H}_2\text{—O—} \\ \text{H} \end{array}\left\{\begin{array}{l}\!\!\text{N} \\ \\ \\ \!\!\text{O;}\end{array}\right.$$

in that it belongs both to the water and ammonia type, shows, for instance, that on the one hand it behaves like a hydrate and on the other as a member of the ammonia type, reacting directly with acids, etc."[37]   ▲

The present practice of drawing "lines" between the units of a complex formula, although originally attributed to Kekulé, was first suggested by Couper.[38] In an unprovidentially delayed publication, COUPER illustrated

[37] A. KEKULÉ, *Annalen der Chemie und Pharmacie*, **106**, 129 (1858); trans. in O. T. Benfey, *Classics in the Theory of Chemical Combination* (New York: Dover Publications, Inc., 1963), p. 124.

[38] Archibald Scott Couper (1831–1892): A student of Würtz. Couper, during his study in Paris, suggested the theory which incorporated the tetravalence of carbon and created the symbolism which is used today to depict the structure of organic compounds. Through an unfortunate series of circumstances, the presentation of the paper in which these suggestions appeared was delayed; meanwhile Kekulé's classic paper containing virtually the same suggestions appeared. After this, Couper disappeared from the chemical world and his health broke, the last 35 years of his life being chemically unproductive.

this symbolism in the following fashion:

▼   "Methylic and ethylic alcohols will be represented by the formulae

$$C\begin{cases} O \ldots OH \\ H^3, \end{cases} \qquad C\begin{cases} O \ldots OH \\ \vdots & \begin{cases} \ldots H^2 \\ C \ldots H^3. \end{cases} \end{cases}$$

"It will easily be seen that for methylic alcohol the limit of combination of the carbon is equal to 4, the carbon in it being combined with 3 of hydrogen and with 1 of oxygen. This oxygen, of which the combining power is equal to 2, is in turn combined with another atom of oxygen, itself united to 1 of hydrogen.

"In the case of ordinary alcohol, each of the two atoms of carbon satisfies its combining power, on the one hand, by uniting with 3 atoms of hydrogen or of hydrogen and oxygen, and, on the other hand, by uniting with the other atom of carbon. The oxygen is combined in the same manner as in the preceding example. In these cases it will be seen that the carbon belongs to the first type, each atom being combined in the second degree.

"In propylic alcohol,

$$C\begin{cases} O \ldots OH \\ H^2 \end{cases}$$
$$\vdots$$
$$C \ldots H^2$$
$$\vdots$$
$$C \ldots H^3,$$

the combining power of the atom of carbon that is situated in the middle is reduced to 2 for hydrogen, since it is combined chemically with each of the two other atoms of carbon."[39]   ▲

Couper's formulations could be used to describe the constitution of a compound, i.e., the arrangement of the units (radicals and atoms) which give rise to the characteristic reactions of the compound. These formulas suggested an orientation of the constituent units with respect to each other in two dimensions, and it was a relatively simple extension of these ideas which led to a consideration of the three-dimensional relationship of these units.

The nature of the forces which hold atoms (or radicals) together was still unknown. The Newtonian concept of electrical forces operating to hold

[39] *Papers by Archibald Scott Couper,* Alembic Club Reprint, No. 21 (Edinburgh: Oliver and Boyd, 1933), p. 11.

atoms in non-ionic compounds together was still the only suggestion that had been presented. Thus, in attempting to describe the course of the reaction between ether and sulfur dioxide, COUPER wrote:

▼ "In the instance before us, it is a certain property of the oxygen which is the cause of the secondary combinate. This property is the affinity which one atom of oxygen in combination always exerts towards another atom of oxygen likewise in combination.

"This affinity is modified by the electric position of the element to which the respective atoms of oxygen are bound. From this property results the fact, that in organic combinates the atoms of oxygen are always found double.

"For instance, the combining limit of oxygen being two, when two

$$\text{molecules of} \quad \begin{array}{l} C^2 \ldots O \ldots \\ \vdots \quad \ldots H^2 \\ C^2 \ldots H^3 \end{array} \quad \text{are set at liberty, the free affinities of the oxygen}$$

instantly produce the union of these molecules. The cause of the union of two molecules of C^2H^3 has been already remarked. In the two cases, the causes of the union of the respective molecules are in so far different, that the one is the result of a property of the carbon, while the other is the result of a property of the oxygen.

"The view here adopted of the nature of oxygen is, I am convinced, alone in conformity with the reactions where the properties of this body develop themselves.

"The vapour of anhydrous sulphuric acid, for instance, is conducted into anhydrous aether. The following will then be the reaction:

$$-S^2 \begin{array}{l} \cdot O \\ \cdot O \\ O^2 \\ O^2 \end{array} \quad \text{entering into communication with} \quad C^4 \ldots \begin{array}{l} O \ldots O \\ \ldots H^5 \quad H^5 \ldots \end{array} C^4, \text{ the}$$

two atoms of the oxygen of the sulphuric acid and the two atoms of the oxygen of the aether (now in presence of each other) being in different (perhaps different electric) conditions, mutually loosen their former affinities and reunite themselves to the (electrically?) different atoms of oxygen of these respective combinates.

"The same principle may naturally be expected to display itself with regard to acids and bases. The oxygen of an acid unites itself to the (electrically?) different oxygen of water."[40] ▲

---

[40] *Ibid.*, p. 26.

It is interesting to note that about seventy years before Couper's suggestions, which contain the essence of modern structural formulas, William Higgins[41] published a manuscript which included diagrams showing atoms linked together by lines. The diagrams were an attempt to visualize the forces of affinity acting between particles. In this respect, HIGGINS wrote:

▼   "It has been already observed, that metals attract dephlogisticated air[42] with greater force than sulphur, and that sulphur attracts it with greater force than light inflammable air.[43] It has likewise been observed, that vitriolic acid[44] and water, mixed in a certain proportion, will calcine metals with greater facility than concentrated vitriolic acid, and that water will have very little effect on metals in a common temperature. These facts, though they may appear contradictory in themselves when slightly considered, may be accounted for on the following principles, and are, in my opinion, inexplicable by any other means whatever.

"Let us suppose iron or zinc to attract dephlogisticated air with the force of 7, sulphur to attract it with the force of $6\frac{7}{8}$, and light inflammable air with the force of $6\frac{5}{8}$. Let us again suppose these to be the utmost forces that can subsist between particle and particle. That is to say, in water dephlogisticated air is retained with the above force, and likewise in volatile vitriolic acid, with the force already mentioned. It is unnecessary to introduce here the aggregate attraction which frequently preserves a neutrality between bodies, as, for instance, between water and zinc, or water and iron. Stating the attractive forces in the above proportion, which I am led to believe is just, from facts already observed, we should imagine that iron or zinc would calcine in water with greater facility than in vitriolic acid; and if some other circumstance did not interfere, it must be the case. This the following will in some degree illustrate.

"Let S be a particle of sulphur, d a particle of dephlogisticated air, which it attracts with the force of $6\frac{7}{8}$ (Figure 3–1), and let the compound be volatile sulphureous acid; here the tie between S and d is greater by $\frac{2}{8}$, than that between the constituent principles of water, which is but $6\frac{5}{8}$. As the attraction of bodies is mutual, let us suppose S to possess one-half of this force, which is $3\frac{7}{16}$, and this to be its utmost exertion, and likewise d to possess the other half, which is $3\frac{7}{16}$ more, which will unite them with the above-mentioned force. Let us suppose another particle of dephlogisticated air D to have a tendency to unite to S, with the force of $3\frac{7}{16}$, in

---

[41] William Higgins (1762/3–1825): Professor of Chemistry at the Royal Dublin Society. At the age of 26, Higgins published a book containing the application of the atomic theory to chemistry.

[42] Oxygen.

[43] Hydrogen.

[44] Sulfuric acid.

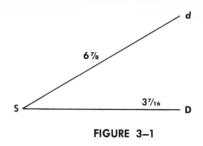

FIGURE 3-1

order to form perfect vitriolic acid: to receive D, S must relax its attraction for d one-half. That is, the force of $3\frac{7}{16}$ will be divided and directed in two different points, which will reduce the attachment of dephlogisticated air and sulphur in perfect vitriolic acid to $5\frac{1}{18}$."[45]   ▲

It is apparent that not only did Higgins anticipate Dalton's atomic theory, but he also touched upon the concept of a bond when he attempted to describe the magnitude of the force acting between two atoms. Presumably the "affinity forces" were considered to act along the "bonds" shown in the diagram. Unfortunately, these ideas were not further pursued by chemists of the times.

SUGGESTED READING

Atkinson, E. R. "The Atomic Hypothesis of William Higgins," *Journal of Chemical Education,* **17,** 3 (1940).

Bykov, G. V. "The Origin of the Theory of Chemical Structure," *Journal of Chemical Education,* **39,** 220 (1962).

"Kekulé-Couper Centennial Symposium," *Journal of Chemical Education,* **36,** 319 (1959). A collection of papers concerned with the various aspects of the structure of carbon compounds.

Leicester, H. M. "Alexander Mikhailovich Butlerov," *Journal of Chemical Education,* **17,** 203 (1940).

Winderlich, R. "Jöns Jakob Berzelius," *Journal of Chemical Education,* **25,** 500 (1948).

[45] W. Higgins, *A Comparative View of the Phlogistic and Antiphlogistic Theories* (London: J. Murray, 1789), p. 38; reprinted in T. S. Wheeler and J. R. Partington, *The Life and Work of William Higgins* (London: Pergamon Press, 1963).

CHAPTER 4

Three-Dimensional Chemistry

When chemists realized that the constitution of compounds was related to the presence of certain reactive groups of atoms, the question of the orientation of these units with respect to each other was considered by various workers. Thus, Gay-Lussac suggested that the difference between cyanic acid and fulminic acid might be explained by "a difference in the connection of the atoms" present in these compounds, and LAURENT went so far as to suggest a three-dimensional model for the substitution theory.

▼   "The first fact which struck me in these substitutions, was the stable condition of equilibrium of the halydes[1]: I perceived these molecular groups reappear incessantly, from the midst of the successive transformations of the first term; I perceived these groups, however great the quantity of chlorine they contained, resist, contrarily to all previous experience, the action of alkalies.

"The instability of the hyperhalydes[2] was not less striking, for all these bodies, however minute the quantity of chlorine they contained, were, on the contrary, attackable by alkalies.

"The next circumstance which astonished me still more, was to see the halydes, hyperhalydes, acids, ethers, alkaloids, and numerous other bodies, conserve their fundamental properties throughout the transformations effected by the action of chlorine — to see certain bodies lose but 1 or 2 per cent. of hydrogen, and gain fifty or sixty per cent. of chlorine or bromine, and yet bear to the bodies from which they were derived, a greater resemblance than is borne by sulphate of iron to sulphate of potash.

"Formerly I expressed these facts by saying, that chlorine, a body so different from hydrogen, might, under certain circumstances, take its *place*

---

[1] Halydes are the products formed when chlorine replaces hydrogen in a compound.
[2] Hyperhalydes are formed from compounds that absorb chlorine without hydrogen replacement.

and fulfil its functions, without changing the arrangement of the atoms of the compounds into which it entered.

"To render my idea more intelligible, I made the following comparison.

"Let us imagine a four-sided prism,[3] of which the eight angles are occupied by eight atoms of carbon, and the centres of the twelve edges by twelve atoms of hydrogen. Let us call this prism the *form* or *fundamental nucleus,* and let us represent it by

$$C^8H^{12}.$$

"If to the bases of the prism, we apply pyramids or atoms of hydrogen, we shall have a hyperhydride; if of chlorine, a hyperhalyde; and if of oxygen, an aldehyde or acid. We will represent the form and composition of these pyramidal prisms thus:

$$C^8H^{12} + H^2$$
$$C^8H^{12} + Cl^2$$
$$C^8H^{12} + O$$
$$C^8H^{12} + O^2.$$

"By certain reactions, we shall be able to slice away the pyramidal portions of the crystal, that is to say, take away its chlorine, oxygen, or excess of hydrogen, and re-obtain the fundamental prism.

"Let us suppose that chlorine, put in presence of this simple prism, removes one of the edges or hydrogen atoms; the prism deprived of this edge would be destroyed, unless it were supplied with some other edge, whether of chlorine, bromine, zinc, &c.; no matter what the nature of the edge, provided it succeeds in maintaining the equilibrium of the other edges and angles. Thus will be formed a new or *derived nucleus* similar to the preceding, and of which the form may be represented by

$$C^8(H^{11}Cl).$$

"If we put this new prism in the presence of chlorine, we may pyramidise it, that is to say, transform it into a hyperhalyde,

$$C^8(H^{11}Cl) + Cl^2;$$

or we may remove from it, another edge of hydrogen. But this must be still replaced by an edge of chlorine, and we shall obtain a new derived prism of which the formula will be[4]

$$C^8(H^{10}Cl^2).”$$

▲

[3] A cube.

[4] A. LAURENT, *Chemical Method, Notation, Classification, and Nomenclature,* trans. W. Odling (London: The Cavendish Society, 1855), pp. 185–190.

Laurent's ideas are illustrated by the geometrical forms shown in Figure 4–1. The creation of a parent substance (or substances) which undergoes reactions to produce new substances that are related chemically, as well as in their arrangements of atoms, was a natural consequence of the attempt to unify the rapidly increasing numbers of apparently unrelated observations.

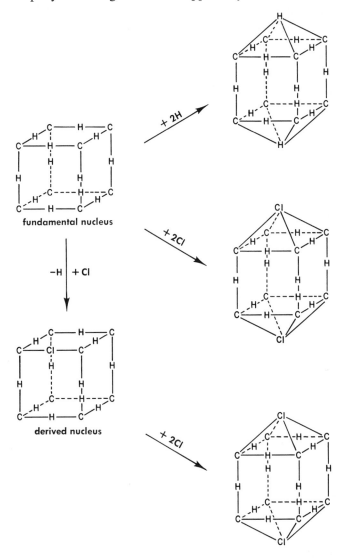

FIGURE 4–1

The geometrical arrangement of atoms in chemically related species according to Laurent.

THE TETRAHEDRAL CARBON ATOM

As the number of known isomeric carbon-containing substances increased, it became apparent that a consideration of the spacial arrangement of atoms in compounds was necessary. Van't Hoff[5] and, several months later, LeBel[6] indicated the answer to the problem of the structure of isomers by suggesting that the carbon atoms in saturated compounds are bound to four other atoms arranged tetrahedrally about them. VAN'T HOFF'S suggestion is succinctly stated in his own words.

▼   "I desire to introduce some remarks which may lead to discussion and hope to avail myself of the discussion to give my ideas more definiteness and breadth. Since the starting point for the following communication is found in the chemistry of the carbon compounds, I shall for the present do nothing more than state the points having reference to it.

"It appears more and more that the present constitutional formulas are incapable of explaining certain cases of isomerism; the reason for this is perhaps the fact that we need a more definite statement about the actual positions of the atoms.

"If we suppose that the atoms lie in a plane, as for example with iso-butyl alcohol (Figure 4–2, a) where the four affinities are represented by four lines in this plane occupying two directions perpendicular to one another, then methane (CH_4) (to start with the simplest case) will give the following isomeric modifications (the different hydrogen atoms being replaced one after the other by univalent groups R′ R″ etc.):

One for $CH_3(R')$	and for	$CH(R')_3$
Two for CH_2R_2',	for	
$CH_2R'R''$,	and for	$CHR_2'R''$
Three for $CHR'R''R'''$	and for	$CR'R''R'''R''''$

(Figure 4–2, b, c, and d); numbers that are clearly greater than the numbers actually known thus far.

"The theory is brought into accord with the facts if we consider the affinities of the carbon atom directed toward the corners of a tetrahedron of which the carbon atom itself occupies the center.

[5] Jacobus Henricus van't Hoff (1852–1911): Professor of Chemistry at Amsterdam (1877) and Berlin (1896) and the first Nobel Laureate in Chemistry (1901). He is noted primarily for recognizing the cause of optical activity and for his description of geometrical isomerism. However, van't Hoff's studies also contributed to elucidating the nature of dilute solutions.

[6] Joseph Achille LeBel (1847–1930): A private research worker, LeBel, along with Pasteur and van't Hoff, is an acknowledged founder of stereochemistry. His studies touched upon the stereochemistry of nitrogen and optical activity.

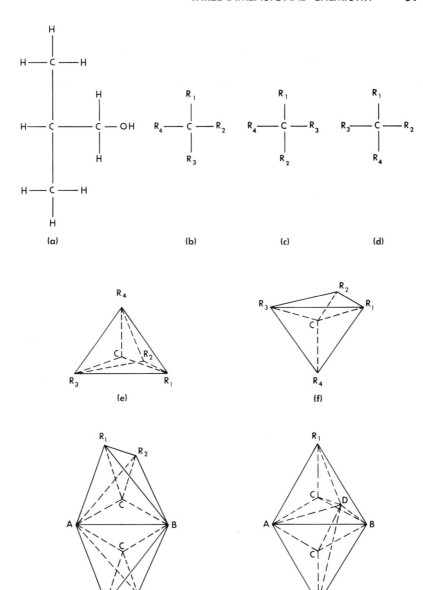

FIGURE 4–2

The figures which van't Hoff used to illustrate his stereochemical ideas.

"The number of isomers is then reduced and will be as follows:

One for CH_3R', CH_2R_2', $CH_2R'R''$, CHR_3',
and $CHR_2'R''$ but
Two for $CHR'R''R$ or more general, for $CR'R''R'''R''''$

"If one imagines himself in the line $R'R'''$ in Figure 4–2, e and 4–2, f
with head toward R' looking toward the line $R''R'''$ then R'' may be on
the right (Figure 4–2, e) or on the left (Figure 4–2, f) of the observer; in
other words: *When the four affinities of the carbon atom are satisfied by
four univalent groups differing among themselves, two and not more than
two different tetrahedrons are obtained, one of which is the reflected image
of the other, they cannot be superposed; that is, we have here to deal with
two structural formulas isomeric in space.* According to this hypothesis the
combination $CR'R''R'''R''''$ presents a condition not presented by the
combinations $CR_2'R''R'''$, $CR_3'R''$ or CR_4', a condition not expressed by
the ordinary mode of representation. According to the present mode there
would be between $CR'R''R'''R''''$ and $CR_2'R''R'''$ a difference quite as
great as between $CR_2'R''R'''$ and $CR_3'R''$, or between $CR_3'R''$ and CR_4'.

"Submitting the first result of this hypothesis to the control of facts, I
believe that it has been thoroughly established that some combinations
which contain a carbon atom combined with four different univalent
groups (such carbon atoms will henceforth be called asymmetric carbon
atoms) present some anomalies in relation to isomerism and other characteristics which are not indicated by the constitutional formulas thus far
used."[7]   ▲

After discussing the relationship between optical activity and geometry,
VAN'T HOFF described the consequences of his tetrahedral model for more
complex structures which involve multiple bonds.

▼   "Thus far we have considered the influence of the hypothesis upon compounds in which the carbon atoms are united by a single affinity only,
(leaving out some aromatic bodies); there remains now to be considered:
  "*The influence of the new hypothesis upon compounds containing
doubly linked carbon atoms.* Double linking is represented by two tetrahedrons with one edge in common (Figure 4–2, g) in which A and B

---

[7] J. H. VAN'T HOFF, *Proposal for the Extension of the Formulas Now in Use in
Chemistry into Space, Together with a Related Remark on the Relation Between the
Optical Rotating Power and the Chemical Constitution of Organic Compounds* (Utrecht:
J. Greven, 1874); trans. in George M. Richardson (ed.), *Foundations of Stereochem-
istry. Memoirs by Pasteur, van't Hoff, LeBel, and Wislicenus* (New York: American
Book Company, 1901), p. 37.

represent the union of the two carbon atoms, and R'R''R'''R'''' represent the univalent groups which saturate the remaining free affinities of the carbon atoms."[8]

"There remain now to be treated carbon atoms which are united by a triple union as in acetylene; this combination is represented by two tetrahedrons with three summits in common or with one of their faces in common (Figure 4–2, h). ACB is the triple union, R' and R'' are the univalent groups which saturate the two remaining affinities of the carbon atoms. The new hypothesis does not in this case lead to any discordance with the views previously held."[9]   ▲

Thus, on the basis of purely chemical observations, and with the aid of a relatively few imaginative minds, chemistry had arrived at the concept of structure and the geometrical relationships which made sense of the apparently endless variety of carbon compounds. Unlike carbon, many of the other elements exhibit variable valence, and this fact was recognized by chemists such as Frankland and Couper. Oddly enough, Kekulé, who with Couper had provided the key to the structure of carbon compounds, resisted the suggestion that an element could have a variable valence.

[8] *Ibid.,* p. 42.
[9] *Ibid.,* p. 44.

CHAPTER 5

The Elements and Their Compounds: Periodicity

The variety of carbon-containing compounds which could easily be obtained made organic chemistry a fruitful area of investigation, and it is logical to expect that the most significant contributions to structure theory at this point should come from studies of these compounds. Evidence was slowly accumulating that the other elements and their compounds could be accommodated into a structural pattern similar to that which had been suggested for carbon. Although there were previous observations of the regularity of the chemical elements, and their compounds had been recognized by numerous chemists, Mendeleev[1] first announced the periodic law as we now know it. The systematization of chemistry as a whole had begun! The basis for MENDELEEV'S arrangement is given in his own words.

▼   ". . . In undertaking to prepare a textbook called "Principles of Chemistry," I wished to establish some sort of system of simple bodies in which their distribution is not guided by chance, as might be thought instinctively, but by some sort of definite and exact principle. We previously saw that there was an almost complete absence of numerical relations for establishing a system of simple bodies, but in the end any system based on numbers which can be determined exactly will deserve preference over other sys-

---

[1] Dimitri Ivanovitsch Mendeleev (1834–1907): Professor of Chemistry at the University of St. Petersburg. Mendeleev is best noted for his discovery of the periodicity of the chemical and physical properties of the elements with respect to their atomic weights. Using the periodic relationship, he accurately predicted the chemical and physical properties of three unknown elements that were later discovered. Mendeleev also investigated the physical properties of liquids and gases.

tems which do not have numerical support, since the former leave little room for arbitrary choices. The numerical data for simple bodies are limited at the present time. If for some of them the physical properties are determined with certainty, yet this applies only to a very small number of the elementary bodies. For example, such properties as optical, or even electrical or magnetic, ones, cannot in the end serve as a support for a system because one and the same body can show different values for these properties, depending on the state in which they occur. In this regard, it is enough to recall graphite and diamond, ordinary and red phosphorus, and oxygen and ozone. Not only do we not know the density in the vapor state for most of them, by which to determine the weight of the particles of the simple bodies, but this density is subject to alteration exactly like those polymeric alterations which have been noted for complex bodies. Oxygen and sulfur show this effect positively, but the relations between nitrogen, phosphorus, and arsenic offer further confirmation because these similar elements have particle weights of N_2, P_4, and As_4, unequal in the number of atoms among themselves. A number of the properties of the simple bodies must change with these polymeric changes. Thus we cannot be sure that for any element, even for platinum, there may not occur another state, and the location of an element in a system based on its physical properties would then be changed. Besides this, anyone understands that no matter how the properties of a simple body may change in the free state, *something* remains constant, and when the elements form compounds, this *something* has a material value and establishes the characteristics of the compounds which include the given element. In this respect, we know only one constant peculiar to an element, namely, the atomic weight. The size of the atomic weight, by the very essence of the matter, is a number which is not related to the state of division of the simple body but to the material part which is common to the simple body and all its compounds. The atomic weight belongs not to coal or the diamond, but to carbon. The property which Gerhardt and Cannizzaro determined as the atomic weight of the elements is based on such a firm and certain assumption that for most bodies, especially for those simple bodies whose heat capacity in the free state has been determined, there remains no doubt of the atomic weight, such as existed some years ago, when the atomic weights were so often confused with the equivalents and determined on the basis of varied and often contradictory ideas."[2]   ▲

We now know that the chemical properties of an element are periodic functions of its atomic number, which is a direct measure of the number

[2] *D. I. Mendeleev, Collected Works,* vol. 2 (Leningrad: Khimteoret, 1934), pp. 3–16; reprinted in *Source Book,* p. 439.

of protons in the nucleus rather than its atomic weight. Fortunately, the atomic weight and the atomic number increase in a regular manner with few exceptions; Mendeleev's basis for the periodic law was in error, but the results are substantially correct. As Mendeleev stated in his Faraday Lecture to The Chemical Society in 1889, "The law of periodicity was thus a direct outcome of the stock of generalizations and established facts which had accumulated by the end of the decade 1860–1870; it is an embodiment of those data in a more or less systematic expression."[3]

In MENDELEEV'S own words, the periodic law is embodied in the following statements.

▼ "1. Elements arranged according to the size of their atomic weights show clear *periodic* properties.

"2. Elements which are similar in chemical function either have atomic weights which lie close together (like Pt, Ir, Os) or show a uniform increase in atomic weight (like K, Rb, Cs). The uniformity of such an increase in the different groups is taken from previous work. In such comparisons, however, the workers did not make use of the conclusions of Gerhardt, Regnault, Cannizzaro, and others who established the true value of the atomic weights of the elements.

"3. Comparisons of the elements or their groups in terms of size of their atomic weights establish their so-called "atomicity" and, to some extent, differences in chemical character, a fact which is clearly evident in the group Li, Be, B, C, N, O, F, and is repeated in the other groups.

"4. The simple bodies which are most widely distributed in nature have small atomic weights, and all the elements which have small atomic weights are characterized by the specialty of their properties. They are therefore the typical elements. Hydrogen, as the lightest element, is in justice chosen as typical of itself.

"5. The *size* of the atomic weight determines the character of the element, just as the size of the molecule determines the properties of the complex body, and so, when we study compounds, we should consider not only the properties and amounts of the elements, not only the reactions, but also the weight of the atoms. Thus, for example, compounds of S and Te, Cl and I, etc., although showing resemblances, also very clearly show differences.

"6. We should still expect to discover many *unknown* simple bodies; for example, those similar to Al and Si, elements with atomic weights of 65 to 75.

---

[3] D. I. Mendeleev, "Faraday Lecture," *Journal of the Chemical Society* (London), **55,** 639 (1889).

"7. Some *analogies* of the elements are discovered from the size of the weights of their atoms. Thus uranium is shown to be analogous to boron and aluminum, a fact which is also justified when their compounds are compared."

"I now present one of many possible systems of elements based on their atomic weights. It serves only as an attempt to express those results which can be obtained in this way. I myself see that this attempt is not final, but it seems to me that it clearly expresses the applicability of my assumptions to all combinations of elements whose atoms are known with certainty. In this I have also wished to establish a general system of the elements. Here is this attempt:[4]

			Ti = 50	Zr = 90	? = 180
			V = 51	Nb = 94	Ta = 182
			Cr = 52	Mo = 96	W = 186
			Mn = 55	Rh = 104,4	Pt = 197,4
			Fe = 56	Ru = 104,4	Ir = 198
		Ni =	Co = 59	Pd = 106,6	Os = 199
H = 1			Cu = 63,4	Ag = 108	Hg = 200
	Be = 9,4	Mg = 24	Zn = 65,2	Cd = 112	
	B = 11	Al = 27,4	? = 68	Ur = 116	Au = 197?
	C = 12	Si = 28	? = 70	Sn = 118	
	N = 14	P = 31	As = 75	Sb = 122	Bi = 210?
	O = 16	S = 32	Se = 79,4	Te = 128?	
	F = 19	Cl = 35,5	Br = 80	J = 127	
Li = 7	Na = 23	K = 39	Rb = 85,4	Cs = 133	Tl = 204
		Ca = 40	Sr = 87,6	Ba = 137	Pb = 207
		? = 45	Ce = 92		
		?Er = 56	La = 94		
		?Yt = 60	Di = 95		
		?In = 75,6	Th = 118?		

▲

Thus, Mendeleev stressed the unity of the elements in a given group (or family), not only in terms of their physical properties but also with respect to their similar chemical function. There was a similarity between the elements of a given group, and a thread of order was observed among elements which were placed in different groups. MENDELEEV continues:

▼   "The regularity and simplicity expressed by the exact laws of crystalline form repeat themselves in the aggregration of the atoms to form molecules. Here, as there, there are but few forms which are essentially different, and their apparent diversity reduces itself to a few fundamental differences of type. There the molecules aggregate themselves into crystalline forms; here, the atoms aggregate themselves into molecular forms or into the types

[4] *D. I. Mendeleev, Collected Works,* vol. 2 (Leningrad: Khimteoret, 1934), pp. 3–16; reprinted in *Source Book,* p. 441.

of compounds. In both cases the fundamental crystalline or molecular forms are liable to variations, conjunctions, and combinations. If we know that potassium gives compounds of the fundamental type KX, where X is a univalent element (which combines with one atom of hydrogen, and is, according to the law of substitution, able to replace it), then we know the composition of its compounds: K_2O, KHO, KCl, NH_2K, KNO_3, K_2SO_4, $KHSO_4$, $K_2Mg(SO_4)_2,6H_2O$, &c. All the possible derivative crystalline forms are not known. So also all the atomic combinations are not known for every element. Thus in the case of potassium, KCH_3, K_3P, K_2Pt, and other like compounds which exist for hydrogen or chlorine are unknown.

"The majority of the fundamental types for the building up of atoms into molecules are already known to us. If X stand for a univalent element, and R for an element combined with it, then eight atomic types may be observed: RX, RX_2, RX_3, RX_4, RX_5, RX_6, RX_7, RX_8. Let X be chlorine or hydrogen. Then examples of the first type will be: H_2, Cl_2, HCl, KCl, NaCl, &c. The compounds of oxygen or calcium may serve as examples of the type R_2X: OH_2, OCl_2, OHCl, CaO, $Ca(OH)_2$, $CaCl_2$, &c. For the third type RX_3 we know the representative NH_3 and the corresponding compounds N_2O_3, NO(OH), NO(OK), PCl_3, P_2O_3, PH_3, SbH_3, Sb_2O_3, B_2O_3, BCl_3, Al_2O_3, &c. The type RX_4 is known among the hydrogen compounds. Marsh gas, CH_4, and its corresponding saturated hydrocarbons, $C_nH_{2n + 2}$, are the best representatives. Also CH_3Cl, CCl_4, $SiCl_4$, $SnCl_4$, SnO_2, CO_2, SiO_2, and a whole series of other compounds come under this class. The type RX_5 is also already familiar to us, but there are no purely hydrogen compounds among its representatives. Sal-ammoniac, NH_4Cl, and the corresponding $NH_4(OH)$, $NO_2(OH)$, $ClO_2(OK)$, as well as PCl_5, $POCl_3$, &c., are representatives of this type. In the higher types also there are no hydrogen compounds, but in the type RX_6 there is the chlorine compound WCl_6, and a fluorine one, SF_6. However, there are many oxygen compounds, and among them SO_3 is the best known representative. To this class also belong $SO_2(OH)_2$, SO_2Cl_2, $SO_2(OH)Cl$, CrO_3, &c., all of an acid character. Of the higher types there are in general only oxygen and acid representatives. The type RX_7 we know in perchloric acid, $ClO_3(OH)$, and potassium permanganate, $MnO_3(OK)$, is also a member. The type RX_8 in a free state is very rare; osmic anhydride, OsO_4, is the best known representative of it."[5]   ▲

At this point a logical extension of the work which had been done in organic chemistry would have been (1) to suggest that the other elements in group IV (i.e., Si, Ge, and Sn) could exhibit a stereochemistry similar to

[5] D. I. MENDELEEV, *Principles of Chemistry*, vol. 2 (London: Longmans, Green, Inc., 1891), p. 10.

that of carbon (for example, in compounds like SiH_4, $GeCl_4$, and $SnCl_4$), and (2) to inquire into the stereochemistry of other simple compounds. Unfortunately, the chemistry of the other elements in group IV was not (and in some instances is still not) studied as extensively as it was for carbon, and the first suggestion was not explicitly made at the time. The question of the stereochemistry of the other elements had to await the development of methods of direct structure determination. Their chemistry did not provide the variety of compounds necessary for geometrical considerations to be made on the basis of arguments derived from purely chemical observations. Future developments along these lines had to await an understanding of the electrical nature of the atom.

SUGGESTED READING

Reinmuth, O. "The Structure of Matter. II. The Periodic Classification of the Elements," *Journal of Chemical Education,* **5,** 1312 (1928). "The Structure of Matter. VI. The Periodic Classification of the Elements Completed," *ibid.,* **6,** 341 (1929).

CHAPTER 6

Electrons and Atomic Structure

The experiments which initiated the sequence of events leading to an understanding of the electrical constitution of atoms were performed by Julius Plücker[1] in 1859, a year after Couper and Kekulé presented their papers clarifying the concept of chemical constitution in general. Few, if any, chemists at the time realized the significance of Plücker's experiment, and it would be about half a century later before the ideas of chemical constitution would be merged with those of the electrical nature of the atom.

Although the development of the experiments and ideas which led to our present understanding of atomic structure is important in its own right, this aspect of the problem must be treated as subordinate to the subject matter of this volume. However, a brief survey of atomic structure is in order at this point in our discussion.[2]

Sir William Crookes[3] suggested that the cathode rays which Plücker discovered in his experiments on the discharge of electricity through gases were composed of particles. Perrin[4] showed that the cathode rays carry a negative electric charge, and J. J. Thomson[5] performed the definitive experiments which confirmed that cathode rays are negatively charged particles with a

---

[1] Julius Plücker (1801–1868): Professor of Mathematics and later of Physics at the University of Bonn. Early in his career he made notable contributions to the field of analytic geometry, but in 1847 he became interested in experimental physics and investigated the magnetic properties of bodies, the action of a magnet on an electrical discharge, and spectral phenomena. In 1865 Plücker abandoned experimental physics as readily as he had mathematics earlier and returned to the study of pure mathematics.

[2] For a more comprehensive discussion, see J. J. Lagowski, *The Structure of Atoms* (Boston: Houghton Mifflin Company, 1963).

[3] Sir William Crookes (1832–1919): A private investigator whose name is associated with many facets of chemistry. He was founder and editor of the *Chemical News* and the discoverer of thallium and uranium X. He also identified the helium found in minerals with that found in the sun's spectrum, investigated electric discharges through gases, and invented the spinthariscope.

small mass, i.e., that they are electrons. Thomson's results are significant because they indicated that atoms contained electrons, and, by implication, that atoms must also contain a positively charged species.

THE NUCLEAR ATOM

Lord Rutherford[6] presented convincing proof that the positive charge in atoms is concentrated in a relatively small portion of the atom; by default, electrons were restricted to the extra-nuclear region. The key to the number of nuclear charges in an atom was supplied by Moseley's[7] X-ray experiments. By studying the X-ray spectra of the elements, Moseley noted that the wave-length of the characteristic radiation proceeds in a regular manner from one element to the next in Mendeleev's periodic arrangement of the elements. MOSELEY's analysis of his data, as well as his interpretation, is best described in his own words which follow.

▼   "A discussion will now be given of the meaning of the wave-lengths of the principal spectrum-line α. In Table 6–1 the values are given of the quantity

$$Q = \sqrt{\frac{\nu}{\frac{3}{4}\nu_0}}$$

[4] Jean Baptiste Perrin (1870–1942): Professor of Physical Chemistry at the Sorbonne. Although he did work on the nature of cathode rays early in his career, Perrin is best known for quantitative confirmation that the Brownian movement is the result of molecular impacts and for the determination of Avogadro's number. In 1926 he won the Nobel Prize in physics for his work.

[5] Sir Joseph John Thomson (1856–1940): Cavendish Professor of Experimental Physics at Cambridge University and Professor of Physics at the Royal Institution. His study of the conduction of electricity through gases led to the discovery and characterization of the electron and the elucidation of the nature of cathode rays as well as to the detection and separation of isotopes. In 1906 he was awarded the Nobel Prize in physics for "recognition of the great services by him in his theoretic and experimental investigations regarding the passage of electricity through gases."

[6] Sir Ernest Rutherford, Baron Rutherford of Nelson (1871–1937): Born in New Zealand, pupil of J. J. Thomson, and Professor at McGill University, Montreal (1898), and at the University of Manchester (1907). Rutherford can be considered as the father of the modern atom. His investigations of the disintegration products of radioactive substances, his elucidation of the nature of the α-particle, and the use of this particle as a "probe" to investigate bulk matter led to the concept of the nuclear atom. Rutherford successfully caused the transmutation of atoms of nitrogen, sodium, aluminum, and phosphorus by bombarding them with α-particles. He received the Nobel Prize in chemistry in 1908 "for his investigation into the disintegration of the elements and the chemistry of radioactive substances."

[7] Henry Gwynn Jefferys Moseley (1887–1915): Moseley studied under Rutherford at Manchester and began to do research at Oxford before World War I. He was twenty-six when he formulated the sequence of elements based upon the atomic number as determined from X-ray experiments. Two years later he was killed on the ill-fated British expedition to the Dardanelles.

v being the frequency of the radiation α, and v_0 the fundamental frequency of ordinary line spectra. The latter is obtained from Rydberg's wave-number, $N_0 = \dfrac{v}{C} = 109{,}720$. The reason for introducing this particular constant will be given later. It is at once evident that Q (Table 6–1) increases by a constant amount as we pass from one element to the next, using the chemical order of the elements in the periodic system. Except in the case of nickel and cobalt, this is also the order of the atomic weights. While, however, Q increases uniformly the atomic weights vary in an arbitrary manner, so that an exception in their order does not come as a surprise. We have here a proof that there is in the atom a fundamental quantity, which

TABLE 6–1

Element	Line	λ	$Q = (v/\tfrac{3}{4}v_0)^{\frac{1}{2}}$	N atomic number	Atomic wt.
Calcium	α	3.368×10^{-8}	19.00	20	40.09
	β	3.094			
Scandium	—	——	——	21	44.1
Titanium	α	2.758	20.99	22	48.1
	β	2.524			
Vanadium	α	2.519	21.96	23	51.06
	β	2.297			
Chromium	α	2.301	22.98	24	52.0
	β	2.093			
Manganese	α	2.111	23.99	25	54.93
	β	1.918			
Iron	α	1.946	24.99	26	55.85
	β	1.765			
Cobalt	α	1.798	26.00	27	58.97
	β	1.629			
Nickel	α	1.662	27.04	28	58.68
	β	1.506			
Copper	α	1.549	28.01	29	63.57
	β	1.402			
Zinc	α	1.445	29.01	30	65.37
	β	1.306			

increases by regular steps as we pass from one element to the next. This quantity can only be the charge on the central positive nucleus, of the existence of which we already have definite proof. Rutherford has shown, from the magnitude of the scattering of α particles by matter, that this nucleus carries a + charge approximately equal to that of A/2 electrons, where A is the atomic weight. Barkla, from the scattering of X-rays by matter, has shown that the number of electrons in an atom is roughly A/2, which for an electrically neutral atom comes to the same thing. Now atomic weights increase on the average by about 2 units at a time, and this strongly suggests the view that N increases from atom to atom always by a single electronic unit. We are therefore led by experiment to the view that N is the same as the number of the place occupied by the element in the periodic system. This atomic number is then H 1, for He 2 for Li 3 . . . for Ca 20 . . . for Zn 30, etc. This theory was originated by Brock and since used by Bohr. We can confidently predict that in the few cases in which the order of the atomic weight A clashes with the chemical order of the periodic system, the chemical properties are governed by N; while A is itself probably a complicated function of N. The very close similarity between the X-ray spectra of the different elements shows that these radiations originate inside the atom, and have no direct connexion with the complicated light-spectra and chemical properties which are governed by the structure of its surface.

"We will now examine the relation

$$Q = \sqrt{\frac{\nu}{\frac{3}{4}\nu_0}}$$

more closely. So far the argument has relied on the fact that Q is a quantity which increases from atom to atom by equal steps. Now Q has been obtained by multiplying $\nu^{\frac{1}{2}}$ by a constant factor so chosen to make the steps equal to unity. We have, therefore,

$$Q = N - k,$$

where k is a constant. Hence the frequency ν varies as $(N - k)^2$. If N for calcium is really 20 then k = 1."[8]   ▲

A variety of new elements had been discovered since the publication of Mendeleev's original periodic chart. In the majority of instances they fit nicely into Mendeleev's premise that the elements are ordered according to increasing atomic weight. Unfortunately, a few elements such as argon and potassium were forced into families with chemical properties markedly different from their own on the basis of their atomic weights. The obvious solution, i.e., that the atomic weights were in error, was not the correct one; however, MOSELEY supplied the correct answer.

▼   "In Figure 6–1 the spectra of the elements are arranged on horizontal lines spaced at equal distances. The order chosen for the elements is the

[8] H. G. J. MOSELEY, "The High Frequency Spectra of the Elements," *Philosophical Magazine,* **26,** 1024 (1913).

order of the atomic weights, except in the cases of A,[9] Co, and Te, where this clashes with the order of the chemical properties. Vacant lines have been left for an element between Mo and Ru, an element between Nd and Sa, and an element between W and Os, none of which are yet known, while Tm, which Welsbach has separated into two constituents, is given two lines. This is equivalent to assigning to successive elements a series of successive characteristic integers. On this principle the integer N for Al, the thirteenth element, has been taken to be 13, and the values of N then assumed by the other elements are given on the left-hand side of Figure 6–1. This proceeding is justified by the fact that it introduces perfect regularity into the X-ray spectra. Examination of Figure 6–1 shows that the values of $v^{\frac{1}{2}}$ for all the lines examined both in the K and the L series now fall on regular curves which approximate to straight lines."[10]

"Now if either the elements were not characterized by these integers, or any mistake had been made in the order chosen or in the number of places left for unknown elements, these regularities would at once disappear. We can therefore conclude from the evidence of the X-ray spectra alone, without using any theory of atomic structure, that these integers are really characteristic of the elements. Further, as it is improbable that two different stable elements should have the same integer, three, and only three, more elements are likely to exist between Al and Au. As the X-ray spectra of these elements can be confidently predicted, they should not be difficult to find."[11]

"From the approximate linear relation between $v^{\frac{1}{2}}$ and N for each line we obtain the general equation

$$v = A(N - b)^2,$$

where A and b are constants characteristic of each line. For the K_α line

$$A = \left(\frac{1}{1^2} - \frac{1}{2^2}\right)v_0 \quad \text{and } b = 1.$$

"For the L_α line approximately

$$A = \left(\frac{1}{2^2} - \frac{1}{3^2}\right)v_0 \quad \text{and } b = 7.4.$$

"The fact that the numbers and arrangement of the lines in the K and L spectra are quite different, strongly suggests that they come from distinct

9 Argon. The present symbol for this element is Ar.
10 H. G. J. MOSELEY, "The High Frequency Spectra of the Elements. Part II," *Philosophical Magazine*, **27**, 709 (1914).
11 *Ibid.*, p. 711.

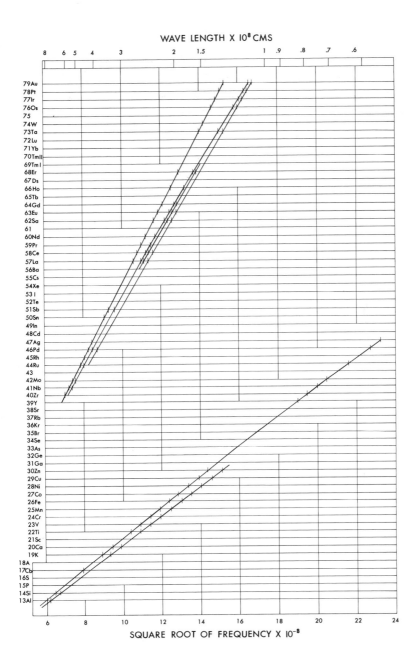

FIGURE 6–1

vibrating systems, while the fact that *b* is much larger for the L lines than for the K lines suggests that the L system is situated the further from the nucleus."[12]   ▲

Thus, when the elements were arranged in order of their atomic number, the anomalies which appeared in Mendeleev's periodic chart based on atomic weights disappeared. It is interesting to note that the atomic number concept which Moseley demonstrated was discussed earlier (1897) by Rydberg.[13] Shortly after the appearance of Moseley's X-ray work, RYDBERG wrote the following:

▼   "After having made use of integers of a similar kind already in the year 1885 in trying to find out the laws of the atomic weights, in 1896 I expressly emphasized the great importance, or rather the necessity, of introducing for the qualities of the elements a true independent variable instead of the atomic weight, which no doubt is not a simple quality but of a most complex nature. As such an independent variable I proposed the *ordinals* of the elements supposing, after the simple rule for the atomic weights of the first elements from He to Cl, that He had the number 2 and Cl the number 17. Finally, having found in 1913 that the system of the elements did not consist of any periods in an ordinary sense, but of quadratic groups of $4p^2$ elements (*p* being the number of the group), I did not doubt that the new numbers (which in the beginning of the series from He onwards were 2 units greater than the old ones) must be the true ordinals of the elements, and therefore ventured to propose that they should be used as rational designations besides the ordinary, as for instance Al (15), Co (29), Ni (30), Ag (49), La (59), Ta (75), Au (81), U (94).

"In the complete coincidence of the order of Mr. Moseley's numbers and of my ordinals of the elements, I see a very strong support of my system, according to which there should be respectively 4, 16, 36, and 64 elements in the four first groups."[14]   ▲

Because Rydberg assumed the existence of two elements between hydrogen and helium, his atomic numbers were two units too large; however, this is the order of the elements which is accepted today.

[12] *Ibid.*, pp. 712–713.

[13] Johannes Rydberg (1854–1919): Professor of Physics at the University of Lund, Sweden. Rydberg's chief interests were spectrum analysis and the relation of elemental spectra to the periodic system. From his work he concluded that "the periodicity of a great number of physical coefficients must depend on the fact that the force which acts between two atoms of the same element is a periodic function of the atomic weight."

[14] J. R. RYDBERG, "The Ordinals of the Elements and the High-Frequency Spectra," *Philosophical Magazine* [6], **28**, 144 (1914).

EXTRA-NUCLEAR ELECTRONS

If Moseley's suggestion that the atomic number represented the number of positive charges in the nucleus of an atom was correct, then the atomic number also represented the number of electrons in the neutral atom. It is apparent that the extra-nuclear electrons would be attracted to the positive nucleus if they were stationary. However, if electrons were allowed to move about the nucleus according to the fundamentals of classical electrodynamic theory, a situation would result in which the electrons continually lose energy and eventually spiral into the nucleus — a deduction which is contrary to fact. This dilemma was surmounted by Niels Bohr[15] in 1915 when he published his theory on the structure of the atom based on the quantum theory. The Bohr theory was modified by Sommerfeld,[16] and by Uhlenbeck and Goudsmit, and was eventually displaced by the wave-mechanical concept of atomic structure.

At this point in our discussion of the concept of a chemical bond, a brief review of Bohr's theory is necessary.[2] The modified Bohr theory explains the spectrum of hydrogen by allowing (quantizing) only certain motions of the electron about the nucleus. The relative energies of the electron in each of these allowed motions can be designated by a quantum number. If the electron moves in an orbit of a given energy, it neither gains nor loses energy. However, an electron can be excited to a higher energy orbit by gaining energy, or it can drop to a lower energy orbit and lose energy in the process. The energy an electron gains or loses as it passes from one orbit to the next is a discrete quantity as determined by the quantum numbers of the orbits involved. Thus, Bohr was able to explain the spectra of the elements in terms of the arrangement of electrons about a nucleus, the excitation of electrons to higher energy orbits, and the release of energy in discrete amounts as electrons fall back to lower orbits. The number of electrons in a given atom was known, and the interpretation of Mendeleev's periodic arrangement of the elements on the basis of the electronic structures of the atoms followed.

[15] Niels Bohr (1885–1962): Professor of Theoretical Physics at the University of Copenhagen. After taking his Ph.D. degree at the University of Copenhagen in 1911, Bohr studied for one year at Cambridge with J. J. Thomson and for one year at Manchester with Ernest Rutherford. Immediately upon his return to Copenhagen he published his famous theory for the structure of the hydrogen atom. In 1937 Bohr suggested a model for the structure of atomic nuclei. He received the Nobel Prize in physics in 1922 "for his services in the investigation of the structure of atoms, and of the radiation emanating from them."

[16] Arnold Johannes Wilhelm Sommerfeld (1868–1951): Professor of Physics at Aachen (1900) and at Munich (1906). Sommerfeld is most noted for his contributions to atomic physics, radiation phenomena, the quantum theory, and the theory of atomic structure. He refined the original Bohr theory considerably by the introduction of elliptical orbits.

SUGGESTED READING

Reinmuth, O. "The Structure of Matter. II. The Periodic Classification of the Elements," *Journal of Chemical Education*, **5,** 1312 (1928). "The Structure of Matter. VI. The Periodic Classification of the Elements Completed," *ibid.*, **6,** 341 (1929).

CHAPTER 7

Electrons and Periodicity

It will be remembered that an alternative to the Rutherford model of the atom, which is accepted today as the correct model, was proposed by J. J. Thomson. Thomson's model considered an atom to be a "sphere of positive electrification in which electrons move." Although this model is inconsistent with certain facts, Thomson extracted from it the germ of an idea which attempted to relate electronic structure to the position of an element in the periodic chart.

Thomson could not consider the problem of describing the distribution of electrons (or as he called them, corpuscles) in three dimensions because of the difficulties inherent in solving the mathematical expressions for this system, and he limited his description to the arrangement of electrons in a plane. He showed that a ring of electrons, equally spaced and revolving about a positive center, would be stable until the number of electrons in the ring exceeded a certain number, and then it would divide into two concentric rings. Addition of electrons to the outer ring would bring it to the limit of its stability, whereupon another ring would be formed. The results of THOMSON's calculations are described in his own words.

▼ "In this way we see that when we have a large number of corpuscles in rapid rotation they will arrange themselves as follows: The corpuscles form a series of rings, the corpuscles in one ring being approximately in a plane at right angles to the axis of rotation, the number of particles in the rings diminishing as the radius of the ring diminishes. If the corpuscles can move at right angles to the plane of their orbit, the rings will be in different planes adjusting themselves so that the repulsion between the rings is balanced by the attraction exerted by the positive electrification of the sphere in which they are placed. We have thus in the first place a sphere of uniform positive electrification, and inside this sphere a number of corpuscles arranged in a series of parallel rings, the number of corpuscles in a ring varying from ring to ring: each corpuscle is travelling at a high speed round the circumference of the ring in which it is situated, and the rings are so arranged that those which contain a large number of corpuscles are near the surface of the sphere, while those in which there are a smaller number of corpuscles are more in the inside."[1]   ▲

Thus, Thomson showed that a given number of electrons would form stable groupings. Although these calculations were made about ten years prior to Moseley's work, it was suspected that atoms of different elements had different numbers of electrons. THOMSON attempted to relate his theoretical calculations to the periodic classification of the elements.

▼   "We suppose that the atom consists of a number of corpuscles moving about in a sphere of uniform positive electrification: the problems we have to solve are (1) what would be the structure of such an atom, *i.e.* how would the corpuscles arrange themselves in the sphere; and (2) what properties would this structure confer upon the atom. The solution of (1) when the corpuscles are constrained to move in one plane is indicated by the results we have just obtained — the corpuscles will arrange themselves in a series of concentric rings. This arrangement is necessitated by the fact that a large number of corpuscles cannot be in stable equilibrium when arranged as a single ring, while this ring can be made stable by placing inside it an appropriate number of corpuscles. When the corpuscles are not constrained to one plane, but can move about in all directions, they will arrange themselves in a series of concentric shells; for we can easily see that, as in the case of the ring, a number of corpuscles distributed over the surface of a shell will not be in stable equilibrium if the number of corpuscles is large, unless there are other corpuscles inside the shell, while the equilibrium can be made stable by introducing within the shell an appropriate number of other corpuscles.

"The analytical and geometrical difficulties of the problem of the distribution of the corpuscles when they are arranged in shells are much greater than when they are arranged in rings, and I have not as yet succeeded in getting a general solution. We can see, however, that the same kind of properties will be associated with the shells as with the rings; and

[1] J. J. THOMSON, "On the Structure of the Atom," *Philosophical Magazine* [6], **1**, 254 (1904).

as our solution of the latter case enables us to give definite results, I shall confine myself to this case, and endeavour to show that the properties conferred on the atom by this ring structure are analogous in many respects to those possessed by the atoms of the chemical elements, and that in particular the properties of the atom will depend upon its atomic weight in a way very analogous to that expressed by the periodic law.

"Let us suppose, then, that we have N corpuscles each carrying a charge *e* of negative electricity, placed in a sphere of positive electrification, the whole charge in the sphere being equal to N*e*; let us find the distribution of the corpuscles when they are arranged in what we may consider to be the simplest way, *i.e.* when the number of rings is a minimum, so that in each ring there are as nearly as possible as many corpuscles as it is possible for the corpuscles inside to hold in equilibrium."[2]   ▲

Following this description of his method of calculation, THOMSON'S conclusion is presented in his own words.

▼   "The following table, which gives the way in which various numbers of corpuscles group themselves, has been calculated in this way; the numbers range downwards from 60 at intervals of 5.

Number of corpuscles	60.	55.	50.	45.	40.	35.
Number in successive rings	20	19	18	17	16	16
	16	16	15	14	13	12
	13	12	11	10	8	6
	8	7	5	4	3	1
	3	1	1			

Number of corpuscles	30.	25.	20.	15.	10.	5.
Number in successive rings	15	13	12	10	8	5
	10	9	7	5	2	
	5	3	1			

"We give also the entire series of arrangement of corpuscles for which the outer ring consists of 20 corpuscles.

Number of corpuscles	59.	60.	61.	62.	63.	64.	65.	66.	67.
Number in successive rings	20	20	20	20	20	20	20	20	20
	16	16	16	17	17	17	17	17	17
	13	13	13	13	13	13	14	14	15
	8	8	9	9	10	10	10	10	10
	2	3	3	3	3	4	4	5	5

[2] *Ibid.*, pp. 255–256.

"59 is the smallest number of corpuscles which can have an outer ring of 20, while when the number of corpuscles is greater than 67 the outer ring will contain more than 20 corpuscles.

"Let us now consider the connexion between these results and the properties possessed by the atoms of the chemical elements. We suppose that the mass of an atom is the sum of the masses of the corpuscles it contains, so that the atomic weight of an element is measured by the number of corpuscles in its atom. An inspection of the results just given will show that systems built up of rings of corpuscles in the way we have described, will possess properties analogous to some of those possessed by the atom. In the first place, we see that the various arrangements of the corpuscles can be classified in families, the grouping of the corpuscles in the various members of the family having certain features in common. Thus, for example, we see that the group of 60 corpuscles consists of the same rings of corpuscles as the group of 40 with an additional ring of 20 corpuscles round it, while the group of 40 consists of the same series of rings as the group of 24 with an additional ring outside, while 24 is the group 11 with an additional ring."[3]

"Thus we see that we can divide the various groups of atoms into series such that each member of the series is derived from the preceding member (*i.e.* the member next below it in atomic weight) by adding to it another ring of corpuscles. We should expect the atoms formed by a series of corpuscles of this kind to have many points of resemblance. Take, for example, the vibrations of the corpuscles; these may be divided into two sets: (1) Those arising from the rotation of the corpuscles around their orbits: if all the corpuscles in one atom have the same angular velocity, the frequency of the vibrations produced by the rotation of the ring of corpuscles is proportional to the number of corpuscles in the ring; and thus in the spectrum of each element in the series there would be a series of frequencies bearing the same ratio to each other, the ratio of the frequencies being the ratios of the numbers in the various rings.

"The second system of vibrations are those arising from the displacement of the ring from its circular figure. If now the distance of a corpuscle in the outer ring from a corpuscle in the collection of rings inside it is great compared with the distance of the second corpuscle from its nearest neighbour on its own ring, the effect of the outer ring of corpuscles on the inner set of rings will only 'disturb' the vibrations of the latter without fundamentally altering the character of their vibrations. Thus for these vibrations, as well as for those due to the rotations, the sequence of frequencies would present much the same features for the various elements in the series; there would be in the spectrum corresponding groups of asso-

[3] *Ibid.*, pp. 257–258.

ciated lines. We regard a series of atoms formed in this way, *i.e.* when the atom of the *p*th member is formed from that of the (*p*–1)th by the addition of a single ring of corpuscles, as belonging to elements in the same group in the arrangement of the elements according to the periodic law; *i.e.*, they form a series which, if arranged according to Mendeléef's table, would all be in the same vertical column."[4]

"Thus, if we consider the series of arrangements of corpuscles having on the outside a ring containing a constant number of corpuscles, we have at the beginning and end systems which behave like the atoms of an element whose atoms are incapable of retaining a charge of either positive or negative electricity; then (proceeding in the order of increasing number of corpuscles) we have first a system which behaves like the atom of a monovalent electropositive element, next one which behaves like the atom of a divalent electropositive element, while at the other end of the series we have a system which behaves like an atom with no valency, immediately preceding this, one which behaves like the atom of a monovalent electronegative element, while this again is preceded by one, behaving like the atom of a divalent electronegative element.

"This sequence of properties is very like that observed in the case of the atoms of the elements.

"Thus we have the series of elements:

| He | Li | Be | B | C | N | O | F | Ne. |
| Ne | Na | Mg | Al | Si | P | S | Cl | Arg. |

"The first and last element in each of these series has no valency, the second is a monovalent electropositive element, the last but one is a monovalent electronegative element, the third is a divalent electropositive element, the last but two a divalent electronegative element, and so on."[5] ▲

Not only did THOMSON see a relationship between the relative stability of rings containing a certain number of electrons and the periodic properties of the elements, but he also anticipated the possibility that elements with unstable rings of electrons could acquire stability by either gaining or losing electrons.

▼ "When atoms like the electronegative ones, in which the corpuscles are very stable, are mixed with atoms like the electropositive ones, in which the corpuscles are not nearly so firmly held, the forces to which the corpuscles are subject by the action of the atoms upon each other may result in the detachment of corpuscles from the electropositive atoms and their

[4] *Ibid.,* p. 259.
[5] *Ibid.,* p. 262.

transference to the electronegative. The electronegative atoms will thus get a charge of negative electricity, the electropositive atoms one of positive, the oppositely charged atoms will attract each other, and a chemical compound of the electropositive and electronegative atoms will be formed.

"Just as an uncharged conducting sphere will by electrostatic induction attract a corpuscle in its neighbourhood, so a corpuscle outside an atom will be attracted, even though the atom has not become positively charged by losing a corpuscle. When the outside corpuscle is dragged into the atom there will be a diminution in the potential energy, the amount of this diminution depending on the number of corpuscles in the atom. If now we have an atom A such that loss of potential energy due to the fall into the atom of a corpuscle from outside is greater than the work required to drag a corpuscle from an atom B of a different kind, then an intimate mixture of A and B atoms will result in the A atoms dragging corpuscles from the B atoms, thus the A atoms will get negatively, the B atoms positively electrified, and the oppositely electrified atoms will combine, forming a compound such as A_-B_+; in such a case as this chemical combination might be expected whenever the atoms were brought into contact. Even when the loss of potential energy when a corpuscle falls into A is less than the work required to drag a corpuscle right away from B, the existence of a suitable physical environment may lead to chemical combination between A and B. For when a corpuscle is dragged out of and away from an atom a considerable portion of the work is spent on the corpuscle after it has left the atom, while of the work gained when a corpuscle falls into an atom, the proportion done outside to that done inside the atom is smaller than the proportion for the corresponding quantities when the corpuscle is dragged out of an atom. Thus, though the work required to move a corpuscle from B to an infinite distance may be greater than that gained when a corpuscle moves from an infinite distance into A, yet the work gained when a corpuscle went from the surface of A into its interior might be greater than the work required to move a corpuscle from the interior to the surface of B. In this case anything which diminished the forces on the corpuscle when they got outside the atom, as, for example, the presence of a medium of great specific inductive capacity such as water, or contact with a metal such as platinum black, would greatly increase the chance of chemical combination."[6]   ▲

It is apparent that, although Thomson's model for the structure of the atom was incorrect, he made certain deductions from this model which contained the basis for the ideas that were developed into the present theory of bonding.

[6] *Ibid.*, pp. 262–263.

THE BOHR-SOMMERFELD THEORY AND CHEMICAL CONSTITUTION

Bohr applied the quantum theory of atomic structure, which had been used with great success to describe the hydrogen spectrum, to more complex atomic systems. Although the simple Bohr-Sommerfeld theory could not be applied directly to these systems, it did provide an insight into the relationship between periodicity and electronic distribution in atoms.

▼   "The common character of theories of atomic constitution has been the endeavour to find configurations and motions of the electrons which would seem to offer an interpretation of the variations of the chemical properties of the elements with the atomic number as they are so clearly exhibited in the well-known periodic law. A consideration of this law leads directly to the view that the electrons in the atom are arranged in distinctly separate groups, each containing a number of electrons equal to one of the periods in the sequence of the elements, arranged according to increasing atomic number. In the first attempts to obtain a definite picture of the configuration and motion of the electrons in these groups it was assumed that the electrons within each group at any moment were placed at equal angular intervals on a circular orbit with the nucleus at the centre, while in later theories this simple assumption has been replaced by the assumptions that the configurations of electrons within the various groups do not possess such simple axial symmetry, but exhibit a higher degree of symmetry in space, it being assumed, for instance, that the configuration of the electrons at any moment during their motions possesses polyhedral symmetry. All such theories involve, however, the fundamental difficulty that no interpretation is given why these configurations actually appear during the formation of the atom through a process of binding of the electrons by the nucleus, and why the constitution of the atom is essentially stable in the sense that the original configuration is reorganised if it be temporarily disturbed by external agencies. If we reckon with no other forces between the particles except the attraction and repulsion due to their electric charges, such an interpretation claims clearly that there must exist an intimate interaction or 'coupling' between the various groups of electrons in the atom which is essentially different from that which might be expected if the electrons in different groups are assumed to move in orbits quite outside each other in such a way that each group may be said to form a 'shell' of the atom, the effect of which on the constitution of the outer shells would arise mainly from the compensation of a part of the attraction from the nucleus due to the charge of the electrons.

"While in this way a detailed interpretation of spectroscopic results of a very different kind has been obtained, so far as phenomena which depend essentially on the motion of one electron in the atom were concerned, no definite elucidation has been obtained with regard to the constitution of atoms containing several electrons, due to the circumstance that the methods of fixing stationary states were not able to remove the arbitrariness in the choice of the number and configurations of the electrons in the various groups, or shells, of the atom. In fact, the only immediate consequence to which they lead is that the motion of every electron in the atom will on a first approximation correspond to one of the stationary states of a system consisting of a particle moving in a central field of force, which in their limit are represented by the various circular or elliptical stationary orbits which appear in Sommerfeld's theory of the fine structure of the hydrogen lines. A way to remove the arbitrariness in question is opened, however, by the introduction of the correspondence principle, which gives expression to the tendency in the quantum theory to see not merely a set of formal rules for fixing the stationary states of atomic systems and the frequency of the radiation emitted by the transitions between these states, but rather an attempt to obtain a rational generalisation of the electro-magnetic theory of radiation which exhibits the discontinuous character necessary to account for the essential stability of atoms.

"Without entering here on a detailed formulation of the correspondence principle, it may be sufficient for the present purpose to say that it establishes an intimate connection between the character of the motion in the stationary states of an atomic system and the possibility of a transition between two of these states, and therefore offers a basis for a theoretical examination of the process which may be expected to take place during the formation and reorganisation of an atom.

"Thus by means of a closer examination of the progress of the binding process this principle offers a simple argument for concluding that these electrons are arranged in groups in a way which reflects the periods exhibited by the chemical properties of the elements within the sequence of increasing atomic numbers. In fact, if we consider the binding of a large number of electrons by a nucleus of high positive charge, this argument suggests that after the first two electrons are bound in one-quantum orbits, the next eight electrons will be bound in two-quanta orbits, the next eighteen in three-quanta orbits, and the next thirty-two in four-quanta orbits.

"Although the arrangements of the orbits of the electrons within these groups will exhibit a remarkable degree of spatial symmetry, the groups cannot be said to form simple shells in the sense in which this expression is generally used as regards atomic constitution. In the first place, the argument involves that the electrons within each group do not all play equivalent parts, but are divided into sub-groups corresponding to the different types of multiple-quanta orbits of the same total number of quanta, which represents the various stationary states of an electron moving in a central field. Thus, corresponding to the fact that in such a system there exist two types of two-quanta orbits, three types of three-quanta orbits, and so on, we are led to the view that the above-mentioned group of eight electrons consists of two sub-groups of four electrons each, the group of eighteen electrons of three sub-groups of six electrons each, and the group of thirty-two electrons of four sub-groups of eight electrons each."[7]

"These general remarks apply to the constitution and stability of all the groups of electrons in the atom. On the other hand, the simple variations indicated above of the number of electrons in the groups and sub-groups of successive shells hold only for that region in the atom where the attraction from the nucleus compared with the repulsion from the electrons possesses a preponderant influence on the motion of each electron. As regards the arrangements of the electrons bound by the atom at a moment when the charges of the previously bound electrons begin to compensate the greater part of the positive charge of the nucleus, we meet with new features, and a consideration of the conditions for the binding process forces us to assume that new, added electrons are bound in orbits of a number of quanta equal to, or fewer than, that of the electrons in groups previously bound, although during the greater part of their revolution they will move outside the electrons in these groups. Such a stop in the increase, or even decrease, in the number of quanta characterising the orbits corresponding to the motion of the electrons in successive shells takes place, in general, when somewhat more than half the total number of electrons is bound. During the progress of the binding process the electrons will at first still be arranged in groups of the indicated constitution, so that groups of three-quanta orbits will again contain eighteen electrons and those of two-quanta orbits eight electrons. In the neutral atom, however, the electrons bound last and most loosely will, in general, not be able to arrange themselves in such a regular way. In fact, on the surface of the atom we meet with groups of the described constitution only in the elements which belong to the family of inactive gases, the members of which from many points of view have also been acknowledged to be a sort of landmark within the natural system of the elements. For the atoms of these elements we must expect the constitutions indicated by the following symbols:

Helium (2_1),	Krypton $(2_1 8_2 18_3 8_2)$,
Neon $(2_1 8_2)$,	Xenon $(2_1 8_2 18_3 18_3 8_2)$,
Argon $(2_1 8_2 8_2)$,	Niton (Radon) $(2_1 8_2 18_3 32_4 18_3 8_2)$,

[7] N. BOHR, "Atomic Structure," *Nature,* **107**, 104 (1921).

where the large figures denote the number of electrons in the groups start-ing from the innermost one, and the small figures the total number of quanta characterising the orbits of electrons within each group.

"These configurations are distinguished by an inherent stability in the sense that it is especially difficult to remove any of the electrons from such atoms so as to form positive ions, and that there will be no tendency for an electron to attach itself to the atom and to form a negative ion. The first effect is due to the large number of electrons in the outermost group; hence the attraction from the nucleus is not compensated to the same ex-tent as in configurations where the outer group consists only of a few elec-trons, as is the case in those families of elements which in the periodic table follow immediately after the elements of the family of the inactive gases, and, as is well known, possess a distinct electro-positive character. The second effect is due to the regular constitution of the outermost group, which prevents a new electron from entering as a further member of this group. In the elements belonging to the families which in the periodic table precede the family of the inactive gases we meet in the neutral atom with configurations of the outermost group of electrons which, on the other hand, exhibit a great tendency to complete themselves by the binding of further electrons, resulting in the formation of negative ions.

"The assumption of the presence of the larger groups in the interior of the atom, which is an immediate consequence of the argument underlying the present theory, appears, however, to offer not merely a more suitable basis for the interpretation of the general properties of the elements, but especially an immediate interpretation of the appearance of such families of elements within the periodic table, where the chemical properties of successive elements differ only very slightly from each other. The existence of such families appears, in fact, as a direct consequence of the formation of groups containing a larger number of electrons in the interior of the atom when proceeding through the sequence of the elements. Thus in the family of the rare earths we may be assumed to be witnessing the successive formation of an inner group of thirty-two electrons at that place in the atom where formerly the corresponding group possessed only eighteen electrons. In a similar way we may suppose the appearance of the iron, palladium, and platinum families to be witnessing stages of the formation of groups of eighteen electrons. Compared with the appearance of the family of the rare earths, however, the conditions are here somewhat more complicated, because we have to do with the formation of a group which lies closer to the surface of the atom, and where, therefore, the rapid increase in the compensation of the nuclear charge during the progress of the binding process plays a greater part. In fact, we have to do in the cases in ques-tion, not, as in the rare earths, with a transformation which in its effects keeps inside one and the same group, and where, therefore, the increase in the number in this group is simply reflected in the number of the elements within the family under consideration, but we are witnesses of a transformation which is accompanied by a confluence of several outer groups of electrons."[8]   ▲

_____

PERIODICITY AND ELECTRONIC STRUCTURE

Bohr established a formalism which, with slight modifications, is in use at the present time; the electronic distribution about a given nucleus is obtained by adding electrons in succession to the energy levels available. Bohr suggested that electrons within a given energy level (orbits, or shells) could be grouped into classes (suborbits, or subshells) on the basis of their characteristic motions. The original Bohr subgroupings of electrons within an energy level were modified independently by J. D. Main-Smith and E. C. Stoner[9]; the former used chemical evidence and the latter physical evidence. This modified relationship between electronic configuration and periodicity is discussed by STONER.

_____

▼   "The scheme for the distribution of electrons among the completed sublevels in atoms proposed by Bohr is based on somewhat arbitrary arguments as to symmetry requirements; it is also incomplete in that all the sub-levels known to exist are not separately considered. It is here suggested that the number of electrons associated with a sub-level is connected with the inner quantum number characterizing it, such a connexion being strongly indicated by the term multiplicity observed for optical spectra. The distribution arrived at in this way necessitates no essential change in the process of atom-building pictured by Bohr; but the final result is somewhat different, in that a greater concentration of electrons in outer subgroups is indicated, and the inner sub-groups are complete at an earlier stage. The available evidence as to the final distribution is discussed, and is not unfavourable to the scheme proposed.

"In the classification adopted, the remarkable feature emerges that the number of electrons in each completed level is equal to double the sum of the inner quantum numbers as assigned, there being in the K, L, M, N levels when complete, 2, 8(2 + 2 + 4), 18(2 + 2 + 4 + 4 + 6), 32 . . . electrons. It is suggested that the number of electrons associated with each sub-level separately is also equal to double the inner quantum number.

[8] *Ibid.*, p. 106.
[9] Edmund Clifton Stoner (1899–   ): Professor of Theoretical Physics at Leeds. Stoner contributed to the theory of the solid state, the magnetic properties of matter, thermodynamics, and statistical mechanics.

The justification for this is discussed below. A summarized periodic table (Table 7–1) is given, which shows the nature of the distribution suggested. In the table the number of electrons in the sub-levels of the atom named on the left is given by the whole of the part of the table above and to the left of the thick line which begins under the atom. Krypton, for example, has 2K, 8L, 18M, and 8N electrons."[10]

TABLE 7–1

Suggested Distribution of Electrons

[The distribution of electrons in the atoms is given by the part of the table above and to the left of the thick lines]

Element	Atomic Number	Level (n).	Sub-Level. (k,i)						
			I	II	III	IV	V	VI	VII
			1, 1	2, 1	2, 2	3, 2	3, 3	4, 3	4, 4
He	2	K (1)	2						
Ne	10	L (2)	2	2	4				
A	18	M (3)	2	2	4	(4	6)		
Kr	36	N (4)	2	2	4	(4	6)	6	8
Xe	54	O (5)	2	2	4	(4	6)		
Nt	86	P (6)	2	2	4				

"Chemical properties depend mainly on the number of electrons in outer I, II, III sub-groups. The distribution proposed is primarily concerned with completed groups rather than their course of development; but a few rather suggestive features of the new scheme, where it diverges from Bohr's, may be mentioned. The course of development strongly indicated

[10] E. C. STONER, "The Distribution of Electrons Among Atomic Levels," *Philosophical Magazine,* **48,** 719 (1924).

TABLE 7–2

Number of Electrons in Outer Sub-Groups

Outer Sub-Group.	Column of Periodic Table and Typical Element.							
	I	II	III	IV	V	VI	VII	VIII
	Na	Mg	Al	Si	P	S	Cl	A
I	1	2	2	2	2	2	2	2
II			1	2	2	2	2	2
III					1	2	3	4

for the L(Li–Ne), M(Na–A), N(Cu–Kr), O(Ag–Xe), P(Au–Nt) sub-groups is shown in Table 7–2.

"A consideration of the electrovalency of the elements as indicated by the halides, for example, provides considerable evidence for a subdivision of electrons among the levels in this way. Thus P is 5-valent, corresponding to all the five outer electrons in PCl_5, but also trivalent in PCl_3 corresponding to the three more loosely-bound ($M_{II} + M_{III}$) electrons. (Similarly, the analogous Sb.)   S forms SF_6, SCl_4, and SCl_2. (There are analogous Se and Te compounds.)   Si and the analogues C, Ge, Sn, Pb all form tetrachlorides, and Sn and Pb dichlorides. I forms ICl_3 and IF_5, and also compounds in which it acts as heptavalent."[11]   ▲

The stage was now set for the assault on the problem of the chemical bond.

THE LEWIS ELECTRONIC THEORY

G. N. Lewis[12] revived the "dualistic theory" of Berzelius which had been used successfully to explain various phenomena observed in inorganic chemistry but which had not been applied to organic compounds because of the difficulty of envisioning how electropositive hydrogen could be replaced by electronegative chlorine. LEWIS took the point of view that the structure of the majority of inorganic compounds represent an extreme case with respect to the structures observed for most organic compounds.

[11] *Ibid.,* p. 734.
[12] Gilbert Newton Lewis (1875–1946): Professor of Chemistry at the University of California. Lewis conducted distinguished investigations in thermodynamics, electrochemistry, and other branches of physical chemistry. He is also noted for his exposition of the nature of the chemical bond and its relationship to the periodic classification of the elements.

▼   "Apparently we must recognize the existence of two types of chemical combination which differ, not merely in degree, but in kind. To illustrate the two types we may choose a salt such as potassium chloride, and a paraffin hydrocarbon such as methane. The first type may be called polar, the second non-polar.

"The first important difference between the two types would be expressed if we should designate them as *mobil* and *immobil,* instead of polar and non-polar. To the non-polar, immobil class belong the characteristic organic compounds that are unreactive, inert, and slow to change into more stable forms, as evidenced by the large number of separable isomers. Inorganic compounds, on the other hand, approach more frequently the ideal polar or mobil type, characterized by extreme reactivity.

"To both types of compounds we should ascribe a sort of molecular structure, but this term doubtless has a very different significance in the two cases. To the immobil compounds we may ascribe a sort of *frame* structure, a fixed arrangement of the atoms within the molecule, which permits us to describe accurately the physical and chemical properties of a substance by a single structural formula. The change from the non-polar to the polar type may be regarded, in a sense, as the collapse of this framework. The non-polar molecule, subjected to changing conditions, maintains essentially a constant arrangement of the atoms; but in the polar molecule the atoms must be regarded as moving freely from one position to another, falling now into one place, now into another, like the bits of glass in a kaleidoscope.

"An evidence of, perhaps indeed a cause of, the mobility of polar compounds, is the freedom of one especially important atom, the atom of electricity or the electron, to move from one position to another. This mobility of the electron is responsible for the striking electrical properties of polar substances. The typical polar compounds are the typical electrophiles.[13] The assumption that in a polar compound free charges exist at certain points in the molecule explains not only the tendency of these substances to form ions, but also their high dielectric constant.

"A neutral body which is oppositly charged at opposit ends will attract a similar body. We should therefore expect polarized molecules to unite more or less firmly with one another to form molecular complexes. The

---

[13] An electrophile is defined as a substance which in the pure state is an electrolytic conductor, which ionizes when dissolved in other solvents, and which permits the ionization of other substances dissolved in it. Sodium chloride is a strong electrophile; water, acetic acid, and ammonia are weaker electrophiles; ether and benzene are very poor electrophiles. There is evidence that the presence of other polar combinations increases the tendency toward polarity. In this way the high ionizing power of polar solvents can be explained, as well as the fact that a complex ion invariably has a higher "electro-affinity" than the simple ion from which it is formed.

formation of the so-called molecular compounds is unknown among strictly non-polar substances. Among polar substances, not only are many complex molecules known, composed of different polar units, but polar molecules of the same kind combine to cause the phenomenon known as association. Thus, for example, the order in the series methane, ether, alcohol, acetic acid, water, represents the order not only of increasing association, but also of increasing tendency to assume the polar form.

"To illustrate the foregoing remarks let us compare the two molecules Cl_2 and I_2. We should expect iodine, as the more positive element, to lose an electron more readily, and this is evidently the case. Indeed liquid iodine is not only an ionizing solvent, but is itself in the pure state a conductor of electricity, showing in all probability the presence in appreciable amount of the ions I^+ and I^-. Iodine, moreover, is decidedly a more mobil compound than chlorine, taking part more rapidly in a large number of reactions, in most of which, however, the actual driving force of the reaction, as measured by the free energy change, is greater in the case of chlorine. Finally iodine shows a far greater ability to form molecular compounds, such, for example, as the polyiodides.

Polar.	Non-polar.
Mobil	Immobil
Inert	Reactive
Condensed structure	Frame structure
Tautomerism	Isomerism
Electrophiles	Non-electrophiles
Ionized	Not ionized
Ionizing solvents	Not ionizing solvents
High dielectric constant	Low dielectric constant
Molecular complexes	No molecular complexes
Association	No association
Abnormal liquids	Normal liquids

"The properties of the polar and non-polar types of combination which have been pointed out in the paper of Bray and Branch and in this paper may be summed up in the preceding table."[14]   ▲

Thus, Lewis laid the foundation for the union of ideas which would embrace all chemical combinations, rather than treat one class of compounds by one theory and another by a different theory. In a later paper, LEWIS elaborated on the significance of the polarity or non-polarity of compounds.

[14] G. N. LEWIS, "Valence and Tautomerism," *Journal of the American Chemical Society,* **35**, 1448 (1913).

▼ "All of these properties with respect to which fundamental distinctions have been made between the two types, and which seem so unconnected, are in fact closely related, and the differences are all due to a single cause. Even before making any more special hypothesis we may very safely assume that the essential difference between the polar and the nonpolar molecule is that, in the former, one or more electrons are held by sufficiently weak constraints so that they may become separated from their former positions in the atom, and in the extreme case pass altogether to another atom, thus producing in the molecule a bipole or multipole of high electrical moment. Thus in an extremely polar molecule, such as that of sodium chloride, it is probable that at least in the great majority of molecules the chlorine atom has acquired a unit negative charge and therefore the sodium atom a unit positive charge, and that the process of ionization consists only in a further separation of these charged parts.

"If then we consider the nonpolar molecule as one in which the electrons belonging to the individual atom are held by such constraints that they do not move far from their normal positions, while in the polar molecule the electrons, being more mobile, so move as to separate the molecule into positive and negative parts, then all the distinguishing properties of the two types of compounds become necessary consequences of this assumption, as we may readily show.

"Thus polar compounds with their mobile parts fall readily into those combinations which represent the very few stable states, while the nonpolar molecules, in which the parts are held by firmer constraints, are inert and unreactive, and can therefore be built up into the numerous complicated structures of organic chemistry. Many organic compounds, especially those containing elements like oxygen and nitrogen, and those which are said to be unsaturated, show at least in some part of the molecule a decidedly polar character.

"When a molecule owing to the displacement of an electron, or electrons, becomes a bipole (or multipole) of high electrical moment, that is, when its charged parts are separated by an appreciable distance, its force of attraction for another molecular bipole will be felt over a considerable intervening distance, and two or more such bipoles will frequently be drawn together into a single aggregate in which the positive part of one molecule is brought as near as possible to the negative part of another. The molecules of a polar substance will therefore not only exhibit an unusually high intermolecular attraction at a distance, but will frequently combine with one another and show the phenomenon known as association. It is indeed the substances which are distinctly polar, like ammonia, water, acids, and alcohols, which constitute, on account of association as well as of high intermolecular attraction, a class of liquids which are called abnormal with respect to numerous properties such as critical point, vapor pressure, heat of vaporization, viscosity, and surface tension.

"Moreover a polar substance will combine with other substances to form those aggregates which are sometimes known as molecular compounds or complexes, and it may so combine with substances which are not of themselves markedly polar, for in the presence of a polar substance all other substances become more polar.

"This important effect of polar molecules in rendering others more polar, to which I called attention in my previous paper, has been discussed in some detail by Thomson. A molecular bipole of small molecular moment, which would scarcely attract a similar molecule, will be very appreciably attracted by a polar molecule or bipole of high moment, and may form with it a double molecule. In this process the weaker bipole stretches and its moment increases. In general, if two molecules combine, or even approach one another, each weakens the constraints which hold together the charge of the other, and the electrical moment of each is increased.

"This increase in the polar character of a molecule when combined with, or in the neighborhood of, other polar molecules is to a remarkable degree cumulative, for when two molecules by their approach or combination become more polar they draw other molecules more strongly towards them, but this still further increases their polar character. This is strikingly illustrated in numerous phenomena. Thus two substances in the gaseous state may differ but little in polar character, but when they are condensed to liquids the differences are frequently enormous.

"The polar character of a substance depends, therefore, not only upon the specific properties of the individual molecules, but also upon what we may call the strength of the polar environment. Without attempting to give any quantitative definition of our terms we may plot, as in Figure 7–1, the degree of polarity of a substance as ordinate and the strength of the polar environment as abscissa. We then have for all substances a curve of the type shown in the figure where the dotted line represents the highest

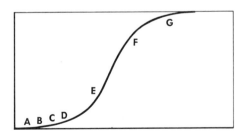

FIGURE 7–1

degree of polarity, namely complete ionization. Different pure substances in the liquid state come at different points, thus, roughly, hexane at A; benzene at B; ether at C; esters at D; water, ammonia, alcohols, amines, acids between D and F; and fused salts at G. In the last case, since the substance has nearly reached its highest possible polarity, it will not be much affected by an increase in the strength of the polar environment. At the other end of the curve a substance at A in a strong polar environment may move to B, and one at B may move to C, but they would not become markedly polar. It is in the intermediate range that substances are most affected by small changes in the environment. Thus hydrochloric acid, which in the pure state is not extremely polar, reaches nearly the highest possible state of polarity when dissolved in water. Such a change in this region is often much accentuated by the formation of complexes, and thus we have the rule of Abegg and Bodländer that a weak electrolyte usually becomes a strong electrolyte when its weak ion is converted into a complex ion.

"We come then to the consideration of the electrical properties which distinguish polar from nonpolar substances, or, in accordance with the terminology which I formerly used, which distinguish good electrophiles from poor electrophiles.

"The first difference is in the dielectric constant. The difference between the dielectric constant of a substance and that of free space measures directly the number of free charges in the substance multiplied by the average distance through which these charges move under the influence of a definite electric field. In the polar molecule the constraints which operate against a separation of the charges, being already weak, may be further stretched in the electric field, and what is more important, the bipoles (or multipoles) which already exist in the polar substance may, by rotation, orient themselves in the electric field, thus producing a large displacement current and therefore a high dielectric constant. In this connection Thomson has called attention to the work of Baedeker, which shows that even in the gaseous state such substances as ammonia, water and hydrochloric acid possess an abnormally high dielectric constant.

"Finally the polar substance, whether in the pure state or dissolved in another solvent, will obviously be the one which will be readily ionized. Moreover, polar substances are the strong ionizing solvents, for when another substance is combined with a highly polar substance, or even dissolved in such a solvent without actual combination of molecules, the degree of its own polarity largely increases.

"Wide apart as the polar and nonpolar types are in the extreme, we must nevertheless inquire whether the difference is one of kind or one of degree. If there were a sharp and always recognizable distinction between the polar and the nonpolar molecule then a substance would be more polar or less polar according as it possessed a greater or smaller percentage of molecules of the first type. This would be a simple and in many cases a satisfactory interpretation of the difference in behavior between different substances, but scanning the whole field of chemical phenomena we are, I believe, forced to the conclusion that the distinction between the most extreme polar and nonpolar types is only one of degree, and that a single molecule, or even a part of a molecule, may pass from one extreme type to another, not by a sudden and discontinuous change, but by imperceptible gradations."[15]   ▲

BONDS, CHARGES, AND ELECTRONIC STRUCTURE

Once it was admitted that a single theory could account for the apparent diversity of chemical compounds, the number of "bonds" in organic compounds (non-polar compounds), the charges on ions in inorganic compounds, the electronic structure of the atoms involved in compound formation, and the position of the atoms in the periodic system were related in Lewis' theory of valence. LEWIS stresses this point in his discussion of the theory.

▼   "Let us turn now to a problem in the solution of which the theory which I am presenting shows its greatest serviceability. The electrochemical theories of Davy and Berzelius were overshadowed by the 'valence' theory when the attention of chemists was largely drawn to the nonpolar substances of organic chemistry. Of late the electrochemical theories have come once more into prominence, but there has always been that antagonism between the two views which invariably results when two rival theories are mutually exclusive, while both contain certain elements of truth. Indeed we may now see that with the interpretation which we are now employing the two theories need not be mutually exclusive, but rather complement one another, for the 'valence' theory, which is the classical basis of structural organic chemistry, deals with the fundamental structure of the molecule, while electrochemical considerations show the influence of positive and negative groups in minor distortions of the fundamental form. Let us consider once for all that by a negative element or radical we mean one which tends to draw towards itself the electron pairs which constitute the outer shells of all neighboring atoms, and that an electropositive group is one that attracts to a less extent, or repels, these electrons. In the majority of carbon compounds there is very little of that separation of the charges which gives a compound a polar character, although certain groups, such as hydroxyl, as well as those containing multiple bonds, not only themselves possess a decidedly polar character, but

[15] G. N. LEWIS, "The Atom and the Molecule," *Journal of the American Chemical Society,* **38,** 764 (1916).

increase, according to principles already discussed, the polar character of all neighboring parts of the molecule. However, in such molecules as methane and carbon tetrachloride, instead of assuming, as in some current theory, that four electrons have definitely left hydrogen for carbon in the first case, and carbon for chlorine in the second, we shall consider that in methane there is a slight movement of the charges toward the carbon so that the carbon is slightly charged negatively, and that in carbon tetra-chloride they are slightly shifted towards the chlorine, leaving the carbon somewhat positive. We must remember that here also we are dealing with averages and that in a few out of many molecules of methane the hydrogen may be negatively charged and the carbon positively.

"In a substance like water the electrons are drawn in from hydrogen to oxygen and we have in the limiting case a certain number of hydrogen atoms which are completely separated as hydrogen ion. The amount of separation of one of the hydrogen atoms, and therefore the degree of ion-ization, will change very greatly when the other hydrogen atom is substi-tuted by a positive or negative group. As a familiar example we may consider acetic acid, in which one hydrogen is replaced by chlorine, $H_2ClCCOOH$. The electrons, being drawn towards the chlorine, permit the pair of electrons joining the methyl and carboxyl groups to approach nearer to the methyl carbon. This pair of electrons, exercising therefore a smaller repulsion upon the other electrons of the hydroxyl oxygen, permit these also to shift in the same direction. In other words, all the electrons move toward the left, producing a greater separation of the electrons from the hydrogen of the hydroxyl, and thus a stronger acid. This simple ex-planation is applicable to a vast number of individual cases. It need only be borne in mind that although the effect of such a displacement of elec-trons at one end of a chain proceeds throughout the whole chain, it be-comes less marked the greater the distance, and the more rigid the con-straints which hold the electrons in the intervening atoms."[16]   ▲

THE LEWIS-KOSSEL THEORY

As is often the case in science, the next step in the development of the concept of the chemical bond was suggested independently by two persons. In 1916 papers by Kossel[17] and by Lewis appeared, almost simultaneously,

[16] *Ibid.*, p. 781.

[17] Walther Ludwig Julius Pachen Heinrich Kossel (1888–1956): Professor of Physics at Kiel (1921), Danzig (1932), and at Tübingen (1947). Kossel's investigations were of prime importance in understanding the electronic structure of the nuclear atom. He was concerned with X-ray emission and absorption, as well as with the problems of valence and molecular structure.

which suggested a model based on the Rutherford atom and indirectly incorporated Bohr's idea that electrons occupy discrete positions with respect to the nucleus. LEWIS stated the postulates of his theory as follows:

▼   "1. In every atom is an essential *kernel* which remains unaltered in all ordinary chemical changes and which possesses an excess of positive charges corresponding in number to the ordinal number of the group in the periodic table to which the element belongs.

"2. The atom is composed of the kernel and an *outer atom* or *shell,* which in the case of the neutral atom, contains negative electrons equal in number to the excess of positive charges of the kernel, but the number of electrons in the shell may vary during chemical change between 0 and 8.

"3. The atom tends to hold an even number of electrons in the shell, and especially to hold eight electrons which are normally arranged symmetrically at the eight corners of a cube.

"4. Two atomic shells are mutually interpenetrable.

"5. Electrons may ordinarily pass with readiness from one position in the outer shell to another. Nevertheless they are held in position by more or less rigid constraints, and these positions and the magnitude of the constraints are determined by the nature of the atom and of such other atoms as are combined with it.

"6. Electric forces between particles which are very close together do not obey the simple law of inverse squares which holds at greater distance."[18]   ▲

The first and second postulates recognize that only the outer (or valence) electrons are important in chemical combinations. The *kernel* contains that portion of the element which is not of interest chemically and is usually represented by the symbol of the element. LEWIS preferred to discuss the number of valence electrons indirectly by describing the number of positive charges on the kernels.

▼   "We have then as kernels with a single positive charge H, Li, Na, K, Rb, Cs; with two positive charges Be, Mg, Ca, Sr, Ba; with three charges B, Al, Sc; with four charges C, Si; with five charges N, P, As, Sb, Bi; with six charges O, S, Se, Te and a group of radioactive isotopes; with seven charges F, Cl, Br, I; and with zero charge He, Ne, A, Kr, Xe, Nt[19]."[20]   ▲

[18] G. N. LEWIS, "The Atom and the Molecule," *Journal of the American Chemical Society,* **38,** 768 (1916).

[19] Radon was called niton, Nt.

[20] G. N. LEWIS, "The Atom and the Molecule," *Journal of the American Chemical Society,* **38,** 769 (1916).

The "even number of electrons" mentioned in Postulate 3 reflects the observation that the total number of electrons in the valence shell of the atoms which constitute a compound is almost always an even number. Chemical compounds which contain an odd number of electrons are relatively unstable with respect to compounds which contain an even number of electrons. For example, nitric oxide (NO), which contains an odd number of valence electrons, readily dimerizes to N_2O_4, which contains an even number of valence electrons.

▼   "Postulate 3 can best be illustrated by the use of formulae in which the electrons of the atomic shells are themselves considered as atoms of the element electricity with the symbol E. Just as with ordinary symbols we use two types of formulae, one the gross formula representing hardly more than the chemical composition of the substance, the other a structural formula in which we attempt to represent the relative positions of the atoms, so we may, with the new symbols, employ the two types of formulae. We shall later discuss the structural formula, but at this point we may consider the gross formula involving the atomic kernels and the electrons of the outer atoms. Lithium has one positive charge in the kernel, fluorine has seven such charges, so that the neutral molecule of lithium fluoride we may represent $LiFE_8$. In lithium sulfate S and O each has six positive charges, and $Li_2SO_4 = Li_2SO_4E_{32}$; $SO_4^{--} = SO_4E_{32}$. In every substance in which each element has either its highest or its lowest polar number, E will appear in multiples of 8. Thus $NH_3 = NH_3E_8$, $H_2O = H_2OE_8$, $KOH = KOHE_8$, $NaNO_3 = NaNO_3E_{24}$, $AlO_3H_3 = AlO_3H_3E_{24}$, $MgCl_2 = MgCl_2E_{16}$, $K_2CO_3 = K_2CO_3E_{24}$. In compounds in which the elements have polar numbers intermediate between the highest and the lowest the number of electrons is not as a rule a multiple of 8, but is in almost all cases *an even number*. Thus $SO_2 = SO_2E_{18}$, $NaClO = NaClOE_{14}$, $C_2H_2 = C_2H_2E_{10}$, $C_6H_6O = C_6H_6OE_{36}$."[21]   ▲

Lewis considered that electrons are added to the nucleus successively to form groups of electrons in concentric shells, the electrons being arranged to occupy the corners of a cube (Figure 7–2, a). Kossel, on the other hand, suggested that the electrons are distributed in concentric rings (Figure 7–2, b). Thus, Lewis envisioned the successive addition of electrons to the same shell (i.e., the formation of the elements in a period) as the completion of a cubical arrangement of electrons (Figure 7–3). Kossel's ideas were similar except that they involved ring structures (Figure 7–4).

[21] *Ibid.*, p. 770.

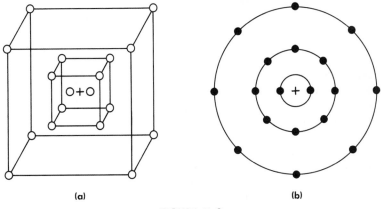

FIGURE 7–2

The arrangement of electrons in argon according to Lewis (a), and Kossel (b).

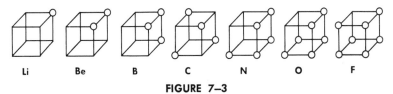

FIGURE 7–3

The electron arrangement in the elements of the second period according to Lewis.

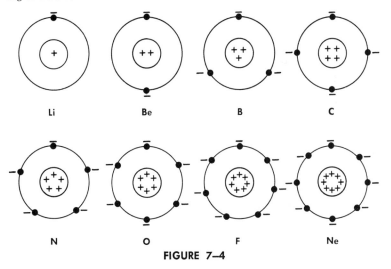

FIGURE 7–4

The electron arrangement in the elements of the second period according to Kossel.

The suggestion in Lewis' third postulate that the valence electrons occupy the corners of a cube would be modified later in considering carbon compounds. Postulate 4 was the basis for the formulation of the covalent bond. Up to this point in our discussion, the formation of ionic (polar) compounds could be rationalized by the complete transfer of electrons from one atom to another to form systems which contain the stable group of eight electrons; Postulate 4 suggested that atoms could acquire the "stable octet" by sharing electrons. This is expressed in LEWIS' words:

▼ "So when calcium and chlorine unite, the calcium atom by giving off two electrons, and each chlorine atom by acquiring one electron, assume the ionic state in which each atom has the group of eight in its outermost shell. However, we have seen that the assumption of such ionizations as a necessary accompaniment to all chemical combinations, even if it is assumed to be only 'intramolecular' ionization, leads to conclusions which are not reconcilable with the facts of chemistry.

"The new theory, *which includes the possibility of complete ionization as a special case,* may be given definite expression as follows: Two atoms may conform to the rule of eight, or the octet rule, not only by the transfer of electrons from one atom to another, but also by sharing one or more pairs of electrons. These electrons which are held in common by two atoms may be considered to belong to the outer shells of both atoms."[22] ▲

Postulate 5 is Lewis' attempt to construct three-dimensional molecules with a static atomic model. LEWIS elaborates on this point in the following:

▼ "Postulate 5 is based upon the fact that we do not find what might be called intra-atomic isomers. If the electrons of the atomic shell could at one time occupy one set of positions and at another time another set, and if there were no opportunity for ready transition from one of these sets of positions to another, we should have a large number of isomers differing from one another only in the situation of the electrons in the atomic shell. While there may possibly be a few cases where we might surmise the existence of just such isomers, in most cases it is evident that they do not exist, and we must assume, therefore, considerable freedom of change from one distribution of electrons in the shell to another."[23]   ▲

[22] G. N. LEWIS, *Valence and the Structure of Atoms and Molecules* (New York: The Chemical Catalog Co., Inc., 1923), p. 69.
[23] G. N. LEWIS, "The Atom and the Molecule," *Journal of the American Chemical Society,* **38,** 772 (1916).

Lewis' basic disagreement with Bohr's dynamic model of atomic structure is reflected in Postulate 6. The rationale for this postulate follows:

▼   "Now there are only two ways in which one body can be held by another. It may, owing to a force of attraction, be drawn toward the second body until this force is gradually offset by a more rapidly increasing force of repulsion. In this case it comes to rest at a point where the net attraction or repulsion is zero, and is therefore in a condition of constraint with respect to any motion along the line joining the two centers; for if the distance between the two bodies is diminished they repel one another, while if the distance is increased they are attracted toward one another. An example of this type is a body attracted toward the earth but resting upon an elastic substance where the attractive force of gravity is offset by the repulsive force which we happen to call elastic; but it would be a mistake to consider the forces of elasticity to be different in character from other known forces. Indeed it is evident that just as we have the law of universal attraction between particles at great distances, so *at small distances* we have the equally universal *law of repulsion*.

"The other way in which one body may hold another is that in which the planets are held by the sun, and this is the way that in some current theories of atomic structure the electrons are supposed to be held by the atom. Such an assumption seems inadequate to explain even the simplest chemical properties of the atom, and I imagine it has been introduced only for the sake of maintaining the laws of electromagnetics which are known to be valid at large distances. The fact is, however, that in the more prominent of these theories even this questionable advantage disappears, for the common laws of electricity are not preserved. The most interesting and suggestive of these theories is the one proposed by Bohr and based upon Planck's quantum theory. Planck in his elementary oscillator which maintains its motion at the absolute zero, and Bohr in his electron moving in a fixed orbit, have invented systems containing electrons of which the motion produces no effect upon external charges. Now this is not only inconsistent with the accepted laws of electromagnetics but, I may add, is logically objectionable, for that state of motion which produces no physical effect whatsoever may better be called a state of rest."[24]   ▲

THE STATIC MODEL OF THE ATOM

By this time the Bohr theory of atomic structure was well established because of its success in predicting accurately the results of a variety of experi-

[24] *Ibid.,* p. 772.

ments. Nonetheless, LEWIS argued for a static atomic model and his reasons are forcefully presented in his own words.

▼   "Now assuming that the electron plays some kind of essential role in the linking together of the atoms within the molecule, and, as far as I am aware, no one conversant with the main facts of chemistry would deny the validity of this assumption, let us consider the typical compounds of old-fashioned organic chemistry in regard to whose molecular structure we already know much — at the very least we may speak definitely of the relative positions of the atoms within their molecules. Among such compounds we find the striking phenomenon of isomerism. Numerous isomers, substances of precisely the same chemical constituents and differing only in the relative order in which the atoms are placed in the molecule, have been prepared. In the case of complex substances, if it were worth while, millions of such isomers could be prepared. Yet these isomers will keep for years, and probably would for centuries, without changing into one another. In these inert organic compounds the atoms are so persistently retained in definite positions in the molecule that in one part of the molecule atoms may be substituted for other atoms and groups for groups, sometimes through reactions of great violence, without disturbing the arrangement of the atoms in some other part of the molecule. It seems inconceivable that electrons which have any part in determining the structure of such a molecule could possess proper motion, whether orbital or chaotic, of any appreciable amplitude. We must assume rather that these electrons are held in the atom in fixed equilibrium positions, about which they may experience minute oscillations under the influence of high temperature or electric discharge, but from which they can not depart very far without altering the structure of any molecule in which the atom is held.

"Let us therefore consider whether the physicists on their part offer any irrefutable arguments in favor of an atomic model of the type of Bohr's. In an atom of the simplest type, composed of a single positive particle and a single electron, if these fail to merge with one another until their centers are coincident — and it is universally assumed that they do not so merge — only two explanations are possible: either the ordinary law of attraction between unlike charges (Coulomb's law) ceases to be valid at very small distances, or the electron must be in sufficiently rapid motion about the atom to offset the force of electric attention. The first of these explanations is the one which I have adopted. The second, which has been adopted largely because it appears to save Coulomb's law, is the one which has led to Bohr's atomic model, in which the electron revolves in definite orbits about the central positive particle. Now it has frequently been pointed out, and indeed it was well recognized by Bohr himself, that this model is not consistent with the established principles of the electromagnetic theory, since in the classical theory a charged particle subjected to any kind of acceleration must radiate energy, while, according to the Bohr hypothesis, radiation occurs only when an electron falls from one stable orbit into another. Since, however, the equation for electromagnetic radiation is one of the more abstruse and less immediate deductions of the classical theory, it might be possible by slight modifications of the fundamental electromagnetic equations to reconcile them with the non-radiation of the orbital electron. I wish therefore to point out a far more fundamental objection to the theory of the revolving electron, due to the fact that Bohr has been forced to assume that this revolution must continue even down to the absolute zero of temperature.

"If, in Figure 7–5, the circle represents the orbit of an electron *B* revolving about the positive center *A*, and if *C* represents a charged particle in the neighborhood, then if the electron exerts any influence whatsoever upon the particle *C*, the latter will be set into sympathetic motion, and a part of the energy of the *atom at the absolute zero* will be contributed to the particle *C*, contrary to the most fundamental principles of thermo-

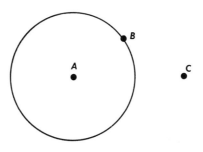

FIGURE 7–5

dynamics. Therefore, unless we are willing, under the onslaught of quantum theories, to throw overboard all of the basic principles of physical science, we must conclude that the electron in the Bohr atom not only ceases to obey Coulomb's law, but exerts no influence whatsoever upon another charged particle at any distance. Yet it is on the basis of Coulomb's law that the equations of Bohr were derived."[25]   ▲

These views were later modified when Lewis accommodated Bohr's atomic model to his theory of molecular structure. LEWIS wrote as follows:

[25] G. N. LEWIS, "The Static Atom," *Science,* **46**, 297 (1917).

▼   "The view based on the periodic law and the chemical behavior of the elements leads to the picture of a relatively static atom. According to this picture, the electrons occupy fixed positions which are arranged in concentric shells about the nucleus. It is not implied that the electrons may not be displaced from these positions by the action of heat and light, or driven into new positions when a chemical reaction occurs. Nor is there anything in this view really incompatible with the assumption of an electron in rapid motion, such as the Parson ring electron, so long as the electron as a whole is regarded as occupying a fixed position in the atom. This theory of the static atom obviously abandoned the assumption that the ordinary laws of electrical attraction and repulsion are valid within the atom.

"The experiments of physicists led to a quite different view of the atom. The theory of Rutherford assumes the forces between the charged particles within the atom to be the same as those which hold for massive charged bodies. The atom is regarded as a sort of planetary system in which the force of attraction between the nucleus and electrons is balanced by the centrifugal force due to their orbital motion. The electrons are considered to be arranged in successive rings rather than in successive shells.

"These two views seemed to be quite incompatible, although it is the same atom that is being investigated by chemist and by physicist. If the electrons are to be regarded as taking an essential part in the process of binding atom to atom in the molecule, it seemed impossible that they could be actuated by the simple laws of force, and travelling in the orbits, required by the planetary theory. The permanence of atomic arrangements, even in very complex molecules, is one of the most striking of chemical phenomena. Isomers maintain their identity for years, often without the slightest appreciable transformation. An organic molecule treated with powerful reagents often suffers radical change in one part of the molecule while the remainder appears to suffer no change. It appears inconceivable that these permanent though essentially unstable configurations could result from the simple law of force embodied in Coulomb's law.

"The first step toward removing barriers between the two types of atomic model was made by Bohr when he restricted the application of Coulomb's law to specific states or orbits. I have attempted to show . . . that it is the orbit as a whole rather than the particular position of the electron within the orbit that is the thing of essential interest in the Bohr theory. If these orbits are in fixed positions and orientations they may be used as the building stones of an atom which has an essentially static character.

"There remained, however, in Bohr's original theory some features which were far from compatible with the chemist's view of the atom. This is essentially true of his models of atoms containing more than one electron. Here he assumed rings of electrons, revolving in a common orbit, which seemed quite irreconcilable with the common phenomena of chemistry.

"Also from the side of physics evidence began to accumulate which was opposed to the ring theory. The X-ray spectrographs obtained from crystals seemed to indicate a cubic or some other regular polyhedral structure of the electrons about the atom, as was shown by the investigations of Hull. A like conclusion was reached by Born and Landé in their searching physico-mathematical investigation of the common physical properties of crystalline substances. These authors, while maintaining the view of the orbital electron, make the orbit small, and make the position of the orbit correspond to the positions assigned to the electrons by Parson and myself.

"In his later work Bohr entirely abandoned the ring of electrons. He found that even the phenomena of spectral lines in the visible and in the X-ray regions could not be interpreted in terms of a theory which regards the electrons as associated with one another in joint orbits. He now assigns to each electron its separate orbit and regards these orbits as situated about the atomic center in shells.

"It seems to me that by this step Bohr has removed every essential element of conflict between the views of the physicist and the chemist. If we regard as the important thing *the orbit as a whole, and not the position of the electron within the orbit,*[26] and if each electron is assigned an independent orbit, then we may think of each electron orbit as having a fixed position in space. The average position of the electron in the orbit may be called the position of the electron and will correspond entirely to that fixed position which was assigned in the theory of the static atom."[27]

▲

The original six postulates were then modified and expanded.

▼   "1. First we shall adopt the whole of Bohr's theory in so far as it pertains to a single atom which possesses a single electron. There are no facts of chemistry which are opposed to this part of the theory, and we thus incorporate in the new model all of the Bohr theory that is strictly quantitative.

"2. In the case of systems containing more than one nucleus or more than one electron, we shall also assume that the electron possesses orbital motion, for such motion seems to be required to account for the phenomenon of magnetism; and each electron in its orbital motion may be

[26] Italics not in the original, but added for emphasis.
[27] G. N. LEWIS, *Valence and the Structure of Atoms and Molecules* (New York: The Chemical Catalog Company, Inc., 1923), p. 55.

regarded as the equivalent of an elementary magnet or magneton. However, in the case of these complex atoms and molecules we shall not assume that an atomic nucleus is necessarily the center or focus of the orbits.

"3. These orbits occupy fixed positions with respect to one another and to the nuclei. When we speak of the position of an electron, we shall refer to the position of the orbit as a whole rather than to the position of the electron within the orbit. With this interpretation, we may state that the change of an electron from one position to another is always accompanied by a finite change of energy. When the positions are such that no change in position of the several parts of the atom or molecule will set free energy, we may say that the system is in the most stable state.

"4. In a process, which consists merely in the fall of an electron from one position to another more stable position, monochromatic radiant energy is emitted, and the frequency of this radiation multiplied by h, the Planck constant, is equal to the difference in the energy of the system between two states.

"5. The electrons of an atom are arranged about the nucleus in concentric shells. The electrons of the outermost shell are spoken of as valence electrons. The valence shell of a free (uncombined) atom never contains more than *eight electrons*. The remainder of the atom, which includes the nucleus and the inner shells, is called the kernel. In the case of the noble gases it is customary to consider that there is no valence shell and that the whole atom is the kernel.

"6. In my paper on 'The Atom and the Molecule' I laid much stress upon the phenomenon of the pairing of electrons. I have since become convinced that this phenomenon is of even greater significance than I then supposed, and that it occurs not only in the valence shell but also within the kernel, and even in the interior of the nucleus itself. It has not seemed desirable to discuss in this book the extremely interesting modern ideas concerning the structure of the atomic nucleus, but if we adopt the old hypothesis of Prout it is possible from the atomic weight and the atomic number alone to determine the number of hydrogen nuclei and the number of electrons which compose the nucleus of a given atom. It is a striking fact that with very few exceptions the number of nuclear electrons so calculated is an even number. It is furthermore to be noted that whenever a radioactive atom emits one beta-particle it almost immediately emits another, again illustrating the instability of an unpaired electron within the nucleus. So also we find that in all the more stable states which atoms assume, the electrons occur in even numbers in the several inner shells. Later we shall show that the valence electrons almost invariably follow the same rule. The simplest explanation of these facts appears to lie in the assumption of a physical pairing of the electrons. There is nothing in the known laws of electric force, nor is there anything in the quantum theory of atomic structure, as far as it has yet been developed, to account for such pairing. However, we have seen that an electron within the atom must be regarded as a magnet, and two such magnets would tend to be drawn together. While the classical theory of magnetism would hardly suffice to account fully for this phenomenon of pairing, there can be no question that the coupling of electrons is intimately connected with the magnetic properties of the electron orbits, and the explanation of this phenomenon must be regarded as one of the most important outstanding problems in quantum theory.

"7. We may next consider a very recent idea advanced by Bohr (1921), which is not based so much upon deductions from his atomic model as upon a direct consideration of the experimental data on spectral series. He assumes essentially that the first shell is associated with a single energy level, and that this level can accommodate one pair of electrons, that the second shell contains two energy levels, each of which is capable of holding two pairs of electrons, making a maximum of eight electrons in the second shell. The third shell has three energy levels, each of which can hold three pairs of electrons, so that the maximum number of electrons in the third shell is eighteen. The fourth shell comprises four levels, each capable of holding four electron pairs, making a total of thirty-two electrons, and so on. We shall see the great utility of this conception as we now proceed to consider the arrangement of electrons in the various elements."[28]   ▲

It is interesting to note that the cubical arrangement of electrons (or vacant positions which an electron might occupy) about an atom is not emphasized in the new postulates.

ELECTRON PAIRING AND MAGNETIC PROPERTIES

The Lewis theory stresses the importance of the pairing of electrons. This concept gained support from the observed magnetic properties of atoms. If each electron in a given molecule is in motion it generates a magnetic field, but, since the vast majority of compounds are diamagnetic, it follows that the magnetic fields associated with the electronic motions have been cancelled. It might be expected that molecules with odd numbers of electrons would exhibit markedly different magnetic properties than those with even numbers of electrons. LEWIS presented this argument in the following words:

[28] *Ibid.,* p. 56.

▼   "In hydrogen the kernel of the atom is the nucleus itself, and there is one valence electron. This single electron should give to the atom a large magnetic moment, and we expect to find that monatomic hydrogen is highly paramagnetic. Unfortunately no one has succeeded in devising an experimental method of ascertaining the susceptibility of the monatomic form, which can only be obtained at very high temperature, or through the agency of a powerful electric discharge.

"In diatomic hydrogen and in helium it was originally assumed by Bohr that the two electrons revolved in the same direction in the same orbit. This would produce a large magnetic moment, and the two gases would therefore be expected to be paramagnetic. On the contrary both gases are diamagnetic, and this model is evidently unsatisfactory. A later model in which the two electrons are placed in separate orbits, making an angle with one another, may be criticized on the same grounds, since this arrangement also should lead to paramagnetism. There are two ways in which a pair of magnets can be held together by their magnetic forces.

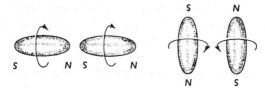

FIGURE 7–6

Two ways in which a pair of magnets may be drawn together.

These are illustrated in Figure 7–6, in which the magnets are represented either as electric circuits or as the equivalent bar magnets. In the first arrangement the two magnets augment one another and produce a magnetic moment greater than that of either magnet alone. In the second arrangement the two magnetic moments neutralize one another, and the lines of magnetic force are almost entirely confined to the immediate neighborhood of the pair of magnets. Since the phenomenon of diamagnetism is predominant in the great majority of substances, we must assume that the second arrangement more nearly represents the normal condition of an electron pair."[29]   ▲

The concept of electron pairs is also a reflection of the electronic arrangement observed in most chemical combinations, both ionic and molecular.

▼   "The discovery that those electrons which are held jointly by two atoms always occur in pairs led to the realization that the 'rule of two' is even

[29] *Ibid.,* p. 58.

more fundamental than the 'rule of eight.' We see at the beginning of the periodic table that helium with its pair of electrons has the same qualities of stability that characterize the remaining rare gases which possess outer octets. Hydrogen may form hydrogen ion with no electrons, it may form hydride ion by adding one electron and thus completing the stable pair, or finally two hydrogen atoms may unite to form the hydrogen molecule, in which each atom shares with the other this stable pair of electrons.

"I called particular attention to the remarkable fact that when we count up the electrons which are comprised in the valence shells of various types of molecules, we find that of some hundred thousand known substances all but a handful contain an even number of such electrons. It is therefore an almost universal rule that the number of valence electrons in a molecule is a multiple of two."[30]

"It is to be supposed that this tendency to form pairs is not a property of free electrons, but rather that it is a property of electrons within the atom. Even within the atom it is not necessary to assume that electrons always exhibit this phenomenon. For example, in the metals of the iron group some of the electrons which seem to be in a condition of great mobility show no evidence of pairing. In nearly all molecules, however, we must consider the electrons as definitely grouped in pairs. In my first theory of the atom I represented the normal group of eight electrons by a cube with an electron at each corner, but the idea that the electrons are coupled leads rather to the view that the stable octet is to be represented rather as a tetrahedron with a pair of electrons at each corner.

"The production of a typical electron pair seems to produce and to be indicated by a state of stability in which electrons are firmly bound. We have agreed to consider the electron within the atom as synonymous with the electron orbit or elementary magnet. The pairing of electrons can therefore be regarded as equivalent to a conjugation of two such orbits accompanied by the neutralization of their magnetic fields and the elimination of magnetic moment."[31]   ▲

THE ELECTRON-PAIR BOND[32]

LEWIS concluded his discourse on the pairing of electrons by defining a chemical bond.

[30] *Ibid.*, p. 79.

[31] *Ibid.*, p. 81.

[32] The concept of the electron-pair bond was applied to a variety of chemical systems by Irving Langmuir which helped him to earn the Nobel Prize in Chemistry. Langmuir's ideas on the subject are presented in the following articles: "The Arrangement of Electrons in Atoms and Molecules," *Journal of the American Chemical Society,* **41,** 868 (1919); "Isomorphism, Isosterism and Covalence," *Journal of the American Chemical Society,* **41,** 1543 (1919).

▼   "Two electrons thus coupled together, when lying between two atomic centers, and held jointly in the shells of the two atoms, I have considered to be the chemical bond. We thus have a concrete picture of that physical entity, that "hook and eye," which is part of the creed of the organic chemist.

"When two atoms of hydrogen join to form the diatomic molecule each furnishes one electron of the pair which constitutes the bond. Representing each valence electron by a dot, we may therefore write as the graphical formula of hydrogen H:H. So when the atom of hydrogen with its one electron unites with the atom of chlorine with its seven electrons, they produce the molecule represented by H:Cl̈:. Two chlorine atoms form the molecule :C̈l:C̈l:.

"To represent the complete structure of the chlorine molecule with its two nuclei and its thirty-four electrons we might draw such a picture as that shown in Figure 7–7. However, such a two-dimensional representa-

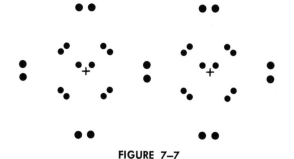

FIGURE 7–7

The arrangement of electrons in the chlorine molecule. (The larger circles represent the valence electrons.)

tion cannot adequately show the spatial configuration of the molecule, nor can we yet locate with any degree of finality the electrons which compose the atomic kernels. We may be sure, however, that each of the outer shells should be represented by a pair of electrons at each corner of a tetrahedron. Such a tetrahedron would ordinarily be regular only in the case of a symmetrical atom like that of carbon in methane, or carbon tetrachloride.

$$H \qquad\qquad\qquad :\ddot{Cl}:$$
$$\overset{\cdot\cdot}{H:C:H} \qquad :\ddot{Cl}:\overset{\cdot\cdot}{C}:\ddot{Cl}:$$
$$\overset{\cdot\cdot}{H} \qquad\qquad\qquad :\ddot{Cl}:$$

"It will, however, only rarely be expedient to indicate in the simple graphical formula any distortion of the octet, although we may assume that it often occurs. Moreover, we must constantly bear in mind as in the case of ordinary formulae of organic chemistry, that our two-dimensional representation fails to represent the true stereochemistry of the molecule.

Thus at first sight the formula for water, H:Ö:H, appears symmetrical, although we really regard the two hydrogens as not symmetrically placed with respect to oxygen, but rather at two corners of a more or less distorted tetrahedron. . . .

"By means of this simple assumption, that the chemical bond is a pair of electrons held jointly by two atoms, I showed how the various types of molecules 'ranging from the extremely polar to the extremely nonpolar' could be interpreted. Quoting from my former paper, 'Great as the difference is between the typical polar and nonpolar substances, we may show how a single molecule may, according to its environment, pass from the extreme polar to the extreme nonpolar form, not *per saltum,* but by imperceptible gradations, as soon as we admit that an electron may be the common property of two atomic shells.' Whether the phrase 'imperceptible gradations' is strictly accurate we shall discuss later.

"The pair of electrons which constitutes the bond may lie between two atomic centers in such a position that there is no electric polarization, or it may be shifted toward one or the other atom in order to give to that atom a negative, and consequently to the other atom a positive charge. But we can no longer speak of any atom as having an integral number of units of charge, except in the case where one atom takes exclusive possession of the bonding pair, and forms an ion.

"For example we may suppose that the normal state of the hydrogen molecule is one in which the electron pair is symmetrically placed between the two atoms. In sodium hydride, on the other hand, we may regard the bonding pair as lying nearer to the hydrogen than to the sodium, making the hydrogen negative; while in hydrochloric acid the bond is shifted toward the chlorine, leaving the hydrogen with a positive charge. In the presence of a polar solvent the chlorine assumes full possession of the bonding pair, and we have complete ionization. I attempted to represent these displacements of electrons by such formulae as

$$H:H, \qquad Na \quad :H, \qquad H \quad :\overset{\cdot\cdot}{\underset{\cdot\cdot}{Cl}}:, \qquad [H]^+ + \left[\, :\overset{\cdot\cdot}{\underset{\cdot\cdot}{Cl}}: \,\right]^-$$

"Even a symmetrical molecule like that of H_2 or I_2 may from time to time become polarized in one direction or the other, as a consequence of the disturbance due to thermal motion. When iodine vapor is heated to a high temperature the molecule breaks in such a way as to sever the bonding pair, and forms two uncharged iodine atoms. On the other hand, in liquid iodine a few of the molecules break apart in another manner. The bonding pair remains intact but remains the exclusive property of one atom, forming I^+ and I^-. These two types of dissociation may be represented as follows:

$$: \overset{\cdot\cdot}{\underset{\cdot\cdot}{I}} : \overset{\cdot\cdot}{\underset{\cdot\cdot}{I}} : \; = \; : \overset{\cdot\cdot}{\underset{\cdot\cdot}{I}} \cdot \; + \; \cdot \overset{\cdot\cdot}{\underset{\cdot\cdot}{I}} : \quad ; \quad : \overset{\cdot\cdot}{\underset{\cdot\cdot}{I}} : \overset{\cdot\cdot}{\underset{\cdot\cdot}{I}} : \; = \; : \overset{\cdot\cdot}{\underset{\cdot\cdot}{I}} \; + \; : \overset{\cdot\cdot}{\underset{\cdot\cdot}{I}} :$$

In other molecules some displacement of electrons may occur without full ionization, thus making the molecule more or less polar.

"Bromine, chlorine, fluorine and hydrogen, in the order named, show a diminishing tendency toward either of the above types of dissociation. We say that the bond in the iodine molecule is looser than the bond in the chlorine molecule. We also say that iodine is a more polar substance than bromine.

"The two ideas are not synonymous, but as a rule the molecule is less polar the tighter the bond. . . . When we speak of a polar substance or a polar molecule we imply either that the molecules are largely polarized, or that they are readily capable of polarization. In other words, we imply that the bonding pair is either displaced in one direction or the other, or that it is easily displaceable, in which case we may say that the pair is mobile. The two things ordinarily go together, but this is not invariably so. The molecule of sodium chloride is highly polarized, but the electron pair is so tightly held by the chlorine atom as to possess little mobility."[33]   ▲

The Lewis concept of the electron-pair bond permitted a better understanding of chemical combination, a problem which had been the source of theoretical difficulties. Prior to the Lewis theory, ammonium chloride had been assigned the structure shown in Figure 7–8 in accord with the observed pen-

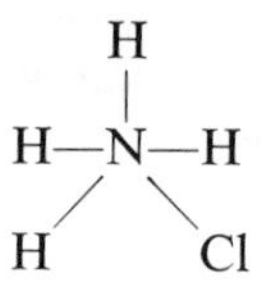

$$\begin{array}{c} H \\ | \\ H-N-H \\ \diagup \quad \diagdown \\ H \qquad Cl \end{array}$$

FIGURE 7–8

tavalence of the Group V elements. However, LEWIS described the constitution of ammonium chloride in the following way.

[33] LEWIS, *op. cit.*, pp. 81–84.

▼   "It is evident that the type of union which we have so far pictured, although it involves two electrons held in common by two atoms, nevertheless corresponds to the single bond as it is commonly used in graphical formulae. In order to illustrate this point further we may discuss a problem which has proved extremely embarrassing to a number of theories of valence. I refer to the structure of ammonia and of ammonium ion. Ammonium ion may of course, on account of the extremely polar character of ammonia and hydrogen ion, be regarded as a loose complex due to the electrical attraction of the two polar molecules. However, as we consider the effect of substituting hydrogen by organic groups we pass gradually into a field where we may be perfectly certain that four groups are attached directly to the nitrogen atom, and these groups are held with sufficient firmness so that numerous stereochemical isomers have been obtained. The solution of this problem in terms of the theory here presented is extremely simple and satisfactory, and it will be sufficient to write an equation in terms of the new symbols in order to make the explanation obvious. Thus for $NH_3 + H^+ = NH_4^+$ we write

$$\begin{array}{ccc} H & & H \\ \cdot\cdot & & \cdot\cdot \\ H : N : + H = & H : N : H \\ \cdot\cdot & & \cdot\cdot \\ H & & H \end{array}$$

When ammonium ion combines with chloride ion the latter is not attached directly to the nitrogen but is held simply through electric forces by the ammonium ion."[34]   ▲

It was fortunate that the octet theory was formulated before the chemistry of the group III elements (boron, aluminum, gallium, indium and thalium) was well established. The atoms of these elements would not be expected to obey the octet theory in the formation of simple compounds [e.g. $B(CH_3)_3$] because they possess only three valence electrons and could attain a share in a maximum of six electrons under ordinary conditions. However, this electron deficiency manifested itself in a number of ways. For example, trivalent boron compounds such as BF_3 and $B(CH_3)_3$ acted as if they were unsaturated (Equations 1 and 2)

$$(CH_3)_3B + NH_3 \rightarrow (CH_3)_3BNH_3 \tag{1}$$

$$BF_3 + NaF \rightarrow NaBF_4 \tag{2}$$

[34] G. N. Lewis, "The Atom and the Molecule," *Journal of the American Chemical Society,* **38,** 777 (1916).

The reaction of two apparently saturated compounds such as $(CH_3)_3B$ and NH_3 (Equation 1) with each other to form a third compound was difficult to understand on the basis of the older valence concepts. In the light of the LEWIS theory this type of interaction now could be readily understood.

▼   "The compounds of boron are of much interest in this connection. Our knowledge of these interesting substances has been greatly clarified by the recent work of Stock. The alkyl compounds of boron have vapor densities corresponding to the simple formula BR_3. Thus we may write for boron trimethyl or triethyl the formula

$$R : \overset{\cdot\cdot}{\underset{\cdot\cdot}{B}} \begin{matrix} R \\ \\ R \end{matrix}$$

There seems to be no way in which boron can have more than three electron pairs in its valence shell. And the properties correspond to the above formula, for boron trialkyl is highly reactive toward any substance which is capable of furnishing the electron pair to complete its octet. Thus with ammonia it forms a compound which remains undissociated when dissolved in benzene. This compound may be represented by the formula

$$R : \overset{\cdot\cdot}{\underset{\cdot\cdot}{B}} : \overset{\cdot\cdot}{\underset{\cdot\cdot}{N}} : H \qquad \begin{matrix} R & H \\ \\ R & H \end{matrix}$$

where a free electron pair of the nitrogen completes the boron octet. In the older valence theory the formation of such a compound would be unintelligible."[35]   ▲

However, a class of compounds exists, exemplified by certain of the compounds of the group III elements, which is not easily understood in terms of the Lewis theory. Diborane, B_2H_6, is perhaps the classic example of an electron-deficient compound. It might be expected that the simplest molecule which could be formed between boron and hydrogen would have the formula BH_3 and that the Lewis formulation would be given by that in Figure 7–9, a. In actual fact, the simplest compound containing boron and hydrogen is di-

[35] G. N. LEWIS, *Valence and the Structure of Atoms and Molecules* (New York: The Chemical Catalog Company, Inc., 1923), p. 98.

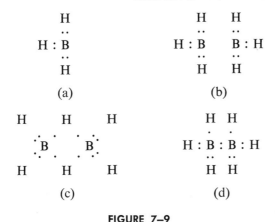

FIGURE 7–9

Lewis formulations for diborane, B₂H₆.

borane, B_2H_6, the dimer of the expected compound. Immediate difficulties arise when an attempt is made to apply the Lewis octet theory to this molecule (Figure 7–9, b); somehow 7 bonds have to be made from twelve electrons. Diborane and other compounds for which not enough electron pairs are present to form all the bonds necessary (in the Lewis sense) are called electron-deficient for obvious reasons. The fact that this type of compound exists (and is exceedingly stable) suggests that perhaps electron-pair bonds are not necessarily the only kinds of bonds that can be formed — they are merely the most common! Suggestions have been made that a one-electron bond may be present in diborane (Figure 7–9, c and d).

Although Lewis is generally credited with explicitly formulating the chemical bond as two electrons shared by two atoms, the electrical nature of bonding in molecular systems had been suggested earlier; to Lewis goes the credit for recognizing the implication of the electron-pair bond with respect to the properties of matter and the periodic system of the elements.

SUGGESTED READING

Luder, W. F. "Electron Configuration as the Basis of the Periodic Table," *Journal of Chemical Education,* **20,** 21 (1943).

Robey, R. F., and Dix, W. M. "Magnetism and Chemical Constitution," *Journal of Chemical Education,* **14,** 414 (1937).

Selwood, P. W. "Molecular Structure and Magnetism," *Journal of Chemical Education,* **19,** 181 (1942).

Wisswesser, W. J. "The Periodic System and Atomic Structure," *Journal of Chemical Education,* **22,** 370 (1945).

CHAPTER 8

The Structural Units of Matter

The arguments presented by Lewis concerning the variation in the physical and chemical properties of compounds led to the suggestion that differences exist in the nature of the "bonds" between the elements from which matter is composed. Consequently, compounds such as sodium chloride were described as "ionic" or "polar," while carbon dioxide and chlorine were considered to be systems in which strong forces held the atoms of a molecule together but relatively weak forces existed between the molecules.

X-RAY DIFFRACTION

In 1913, Max von Laue[1] described experiments on the diffraction of X-rays which would eventually lead to an experimental method for establishing the arrangement of atoms in a crystalline substance. Knowing the positions of atoms in a variety of substances would lead to a clearer understanding of the nature of the forces which bind atoms together, as well as provide a direct answer to the question of the existence of molecules. Thus, the discovery of the diffraction of X-rays eventually proved to be the method by which many of Lewis' ideas were verified.

In Laue's experiment a thin beam of X-rays was allowed to fall on a crystal; the scattering of the X-rays which passed through the crystal was then detected by their action on a photographic plate placed at right angles to the beam a short distance behind the crystal (Figure 8–1). Instead of observ-

---

[1] Max Theodor Felix von Laue (1879–1960): Professor of Physics at Zürich (1912), Frankfurt on Main (1914), Berlin (1919), and Göttingen. Laue's research interests were in the thermodynamics of radiation, optics (including X-ray optics), relativity theory, and superconductivity. He won the Nobel Prize for physics in 1914 "for his discovery of the diffraction of X-rays in crystals."

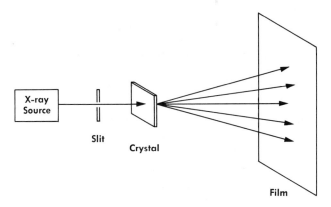

FIGURE 8–1

The diffraction of X-rays by crystals.

ing a general scattering of the X-ray beam, Laue saw a regular pattern of spots appear on the film (Figure 8–2). Laue's original interpretation of this phenomena, together with a simpler explanation, is given by Bragg.[2]

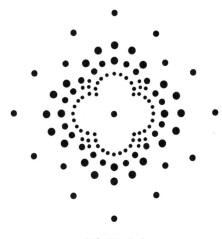

FIGURE 8–2

A typical pattern of spots obtained from an X-ray diffraction experiment.

[2] Sir William Lawrence Bragg (1890–   ): Professor of Physics at Victoria University, Manchester (1919), and at Cambridge. He is best known for his work in the application of X-ray techniques to the determination of atomic positions in a variety of substances. In 1915 he shared the Nobel Prize for physics with his father, W. H. Bragg.

▼ "Herren Friedrich, Knipping, and Laue have lately published a paper entitled 'Interference Phenomena with Röntgen Rays,' the experiments which form the subject of the paper being carried out in the following way (Figure 8–1). A very narrow pencil of rays from an X-ray bulb is isolated by a series of lead screens pierced with fine holes. In the path of this beam is set a small slip of crystal, and a photographic plate is placed a few centimetres behind the crystal at right angles to the beam. When the plate is developed, there appears on it, as well as the intense spot caused by the undeviated X-rays, a series of fainter spots forming an intricate geometrical pattern (Figure 8–2). By moving the photographic plate backwards or forwards it can be seen that these spots are formed by rectilinear pencils spreading in all directions from the crystal, some of them making an angle of over 45° with the direction of the incident radiation.

"When the crystal is a specimen of cubical zinc blende, and one of its three principal cubic axes is set parallel to the incident beam, the pattern of spots is symmetrical about the two remaining axes. Laue's theory of the formation of this pattern is as follows. He considers the molecules of the crystal to form a three-dimensional grating, each molecule being capable of emitting secondary vibrations when struck by incident electromagnetic waves from the X-ray bulb. He places the molecules in the simplest possible of the three cubical point systems, that is, molecules arranged in space in a pattern whose element is a little cube of side 'a,' with a molecule at each corner. He takes coordinate axes whose origin is at a point in the crystal and which are parallel to the sides of the cubes. The incident waves are propagated in a direction parallel to the z axis, and on account of the narrowness of the beam the wave surfaces may be taken to be parallel to the xy plane. The spots are considered to be interference maxima of the waves scattered by the orderly arrangement of molecules in the crystal. In order to get an interference maximum in the direction whose cosines are α, β, γ, for incident radiation of wave-length λ, the following equations must be satisfied

$$a\alpha = h_1\lambda, \ a\beta = h_2\lambda, \ a(1 - \gamma) = h_3\lambda \qquad (1)$$

where $h_1 h_2 h_3$ are integers."[3]

"I think it is possible to explain the formation of the interference pattern without assuming that the incident radiation consists of merely a small number of wave-lengths. The explanation which I propose, on the con-

---

[3] W. L. BRAGG, "The Diffraction of Short Electromagnetic Waves by a Crystal," *Cambridge Philosophical Society Proceedings,* **17**, 43 (1913).

trary, assumes the existence of a continuous spectrum over a wide range in the incident radiation, and the action of the crystal as a diffraction grating will be considered from a different point of view which leads to some simplification.

"Regard the incident light as being composed of a number of independent pulses . . . When a pulse falls on a plane it is reflected. If it falls on a number of particles scattered over a plane which are capable of acting as centres of disturbance when struck by the incident pulse, the secondary waves from them will build up a wave front, exactly as if part of the pulse had been reflected from the plane, as in Huygen's construction for a reflected wave.

"The atoms composing the crystal may be arranged in a great many ways in systems of parallel planes, the simplest being the cleavage planes of the crystal. I propose to regard each interference maximum as due to the reflection of the pulses in the incident beam in one of these systems. Consider the crystal as divided up in this way into a set of parallel planes. A minute fraction of the energy of a pulse traversing the crystal will be reflected from each plane in succession, and the corresponding interference maximum will be produced by a train of reflected pulses. The pulses in the train follow each other at intervals of $2d \cos \theta$, where θ is the angle of incidence of the primary rays on the plane, d is the shortest distance between successive identical planes in the crystal. Considered thus, the crystal actually 'manufactures' light of definite wave-lengths, much as, according to Schuster, a diffraction grating does. The difference in this case lies in the extremely short length of the waves. Each incident pulse produces a train of pulses and this train is resolvable into a series of wave-lengths

$\lambda, \dfrac{\lambda}{2}, \dfrac{\lambda}{3}, \dfrac{\lambda}{4}$ etc., where $\lambda = 2d \cos \theta$."[4]   ▲

It should be noted that the magnitude of the diffraction is dependent upon the distance between the atoms (the diffracting planes) and that the pattern of spots varies with the angle of incidence the beam makes with the diffracting system. Very soon after the discovery of the phenomena of X-ray diffraction, the experimental and theoretical details were developed to the point where it was possible to determine the relative positions of the atoms in a crystalline substance by studying the patterns and relative intensities of the diffracted beams. This technique was used to determine the structure of a variety of crystalline compounds. Many laboratories contributed to the accumulation of such structural data, and a pattern of results began to develop, as described so succinctly by WYCKOFF.

[4] *Ibid.*, p. 45.

▼   "In spite of the obvious characteristics that pervade all these discussions there seems to be considerable evidence, from a consideration of the crystal structures of such compounds as have been more or less carefully studied, for the existence of two distinct types of solid compound — (1) *polar compounds* [ions], wherein the bonding between the atoms, or at least between certain groups of atoms, is polar; and (2) *valence compounds,* the atoms of which are bound to other atoms by holding electrons in common. A consideration of organic compounds, none of which have thus far been successfully studied using X-rays, forces us to a third kind of compound; (3) the *molecule-forming compounds,* built up of groups of atoms (the chemical molecules) held together presumably by relatively weak stray fields of force. It will be noticed that in solids of the first two types no molecules in the chemical sense of the word exist: each crystal is a single chemical individual."[5]   ▲

IONIC COMPOUNDS

The group of compounds which Lewis classified as polar generally have relatively high melting points, high boiling points, and are relatively hard. Sodium chloride, potassium chloride, and sodium nitrate are among the compounds in this class. BRAGG's description of the arrangement of atoms in sodium chloride (Figure 8–3) follows.

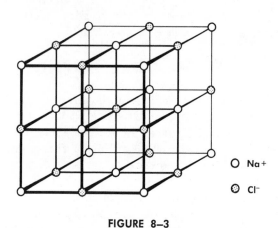

O Na+

⊕ Cl⁻

FIGURE 8–3

The arrangement of ions in crystalline sodium chloride.

[5] R. W. G. WYCKOFF, "The Determination of the Structure of Crystals," *Franklin Institute Journal,* **191,** 230 (1921).

▼   "In the crystal of sodium chloride, the sodium atoms may be regarded as arranged at the corners and face-centres of the unit cube, the chlorine atoms being situated at the centres of the cube-edges and at the centre of the cube. Every sodium atom is surrounded symmetrically by six chlorine atoms, every chlorine atom by six sodium atoms."[6]   ▲

The structure of potassium chloride is the same as that of sodium chloride, the potassium atoms replacing the sodium atoms shown in Figure 8–3. Bragg related these observed structures to the Lewis theory of compound formation in the following way.

▼   "The potassium atom has a nuclear charge of 19 units, and is surrounded by 18 electrons arranged in the same way as those of the argon atom, with, in addition, an electron which finds no place in the stable argon arrangement. Chlorine has a nuclear charge of 17, and is surrounded by 17 electrons, one less than the number required to form the stable argon arrangement. When an atom of potassium combines with one of chlorine, the chlorine atom absorbs into its system the additional electron from the potassium atom. Both atoms are now surrounded by the argon shells, but as the nuclear charges are 19 and 17, and each atom is surrounded by 18 electrons, there will be a resultant positive charge of one unit on the potassium atom and a negative charge of one unit on the chlorine atom. The electrostatic attraction of these charges holds the molecule together. The nuclei, surrounded by the stable argon shells, compose the mono-valent kations and anions of potassium and chlorine."[7]

"The crystalline structure of a compound such as KCl is very simply explained by this theory. As has been pointed out by Langmuir, the crystal is to be regarded as an assemblage of potassium and chlorine ions arranged on a cubic lattice. The ions consist of the stable argon shells, but as the nuclear charges are 19 and 17 the ions have resultant unit positive and negative charges. Each ion tends to surround itself with as many ions of the opposite sign as possible. This is realised in the KCl structure, where each ion is surrounded by six ions of the opposite sign. There are no individual molecules in the crystal structure, the potassium ion has exactly the same relation to the six chlorine ions surrounding it, and *vice versa*. Some repulsive force must exist between the outer shells, which holds the atoms apart against the electrostatic attraction."[8]

[6] W. L. Bragg, "The Arrangement of Atoms in Crystals," *Philosophical Magazine* [6], **40,** 169 (1920).
[7] *Ibid.,* p. 182.
[8] *Ibid.,* p. 183.

"These ions, originally postulated to explain the phenomena of electrolytic conduction in solution, exist also in the solid state. Instead of supposing that the atoms acquire their charges when the salt is dissolved in water, we must now picture the process as a breaking up of the crystal lattice which already consists of negative and positive ions, as was surmised many years ago by Berzelius. Such a structure explains the regular alternation of the atoms, and the non-existence of a grouping into pairs corresponding to 'molecules of sodium chloride.' Molecule association may exist in the state of vapour, but there is no indication of it in the solid state of such compounds. Each ion is immediately surrounded by six of the opposite sign, to all of which it is equally related; the equality in numbers of the two kinds of ion is not the result of molecular association, but of the condition that positive and negative charges must be equivalent in amount throughout the crystal."[9]   ▲

Sodium nitrate has the properties attributed to ionic systems; however, BRAGG pointed out that a new feature was apparent in the structure of this compound.

▼   "In sodium nitrate there is the same arrangement of positive and negative ions as in sodium chloride, except that the negative ion in this case is the complex NO_3 group. In order to complete a stable arrangement around the four nuclei, the NO_3 group has borrowed an electron from the sodium atom, leaving it a positively charged ion. These ions are arranged in the same way in $NaNO_3$ and $NaCl$, each ion being surrounded by six of the opposite sign. The form of the NO_3 group has, however, distorted the structure so that the crystal is rhombohedral instead of cubic."[10]   ▲

It was now recognized that the nitrate group (NO_3) was playing the role of an ion in the crystal structure and that the bonding of the units in solid sodium nitrate was electrostatic. However, it should be noted that the bonding between the nitrogen and oxygen atoms which constitute the nitrate ion is something other than electrostatic, i.e., it arises because of a sharing of electrons between the atoms. Thus it was obvious that two types of bonds must be accounted for in sodium nitrate or in any of the metallic salts of the ternary acids.

[9] SIR LAWRENCE BRAGG, *The Crystalline State: Volume I. A General Survey* (London: G. Bell and Sons, Ltd., 1949), p. 112.

[10] W. L. BRAGG, "The Arrangement of Atoms in Crystals," *Philosophical Magazine* [6], **10**, 184 (1920).

MOLECULAR CRYSTALS

Although the existence of a covalently bound unit was observed in the structure of sodium nitrate, this unit carried a charge and was retained in the structure through the action of electrostatic forces. A study of the structure of organic compounds by Sir W. H. Bragg[11] provided direct proof for the existence of molecules. The first structure reported for an organic compound was that of naphthalene, $C_{10}H_8$. On the basis of chemical evidence painstakingly collected over many years, naphthalene was assigned the structure shown in Figure 8–4; all atoms were supposed to lie in the same plane.

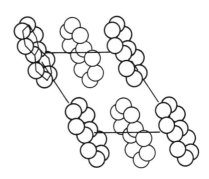

FIGURE 8–4

The molecular structure of naphthalene.

FIGURE 8–5

The structure of naphthalene. Only the carbon atoms are shown.

The arrangement of the atoms in a crystal of naphthalene (Figure 8–5) was shown by Bragg using X-ray analysis.[12] The distance between adjacent carbon atoms within the same molecule was determined to be 1.41 Å, whereas the shortest distance between carbon atoms of adjacent molecules was 3.60 Å.[13] Clearly, there is a preferential association between the carbon atoms within one molecule as compared to that between the carbon atoms of neighboring molecules. The short carbon-carbon distances were assigned to covalent bonds, but the very fact that naphthalene crystallizes with a regular orientation of the molecules suggested the existence of weaker forces be-

[11] Sir William Henry Bragg (1862–1942): Professor of Physics at Adelaide (1886), Leeds (1909), University College, London (1915). Originally, Bragg exhibited a keen interest in the study of electrons and radioactivity, but he is best known for his research on X-rays. Bragg shared the Nobel Prize for Physics in 1915 with his son, W. L. Bragg, "for their merits in the study of crystal structure by means of X-rays."

[12] Sir W. H. Bragg, "Structure of Organic Crystals," *Proceedings of the Physical Society of London,* **34,** 33 (1921).

[13] J. Monteath Robertson, "Crystalline Structure of Naphthalene," *Proceedings of the Royal Society,* **142,** 674 (1933).

tween the molecules. BRAGG concludes his paper with the following words:

▼ "We see clearly that the forces that bind atoms together are of more than one kind. The very strong valency bonds, whether explained as due to electron sharing, or in any other way, are exemplified by all the linkings in diamond and by the linkings in the planes of the graphite flakes. But, besides these are other bonds of much weaker character, such as those extending between an atom in one graphite sheet and its three nearest neighbours in the next. Such bonds as these unite the molecules of the organic compound so as to form the crystal. They are of varying degrees of strength; the cleavage plane shows where they are weakest. They are definitely associated with special points on the molecule as we see from the facts of crystallisation. When a crystal forms in a liquid, or by sublimation, the molecule that attaches itself correctly, and with proper orientation to others already in position, is the one that stays there and resists the tendencies of other drifting and thermally-agitated molecules to remove it. It is fixed by the attachment of certain points on its own structure to certain points on the structure of the other molecules. The beautiful exactness of crystal structure is evidence of the precision with which this adjustment is made; and at the same time of the definite molecular form without which precision would be impossible."[14]

"The arrangement of molecules in crystals or in surface films or interfaces between liquids and solids cannot be fully explained as due to forces which are merely functions of the distances between their centres. Confining ourselves to the cases where there is no obvious separation of electron charges, as there is none in the crystals described above, it is clear that we must think of the molecules as bodies of very definite form. These attachments to one another are made at definite points and the forces there exerted may have very short ranges. The molecules are locked into crystalline structure, when attachments are made at sufficient points, and the whole has the stability of an engineering structure. It may well be that in a liquid there are always some completed attachments, but insufficient in number to give rigidity to the whole. In a gas there are no attachments at all."[15]   ▲

GIANT MOLECULES

In contrast to the discrete units which make up molecular crystals and are held together by relatively weak forces, other substances such as diamond

[14] SIR W. H. BRAGG, "Structure of Organic Crystals," *Proceedings of the Physical Society of London,* **34,** 49 (1901).
[15] *Ibid.,* p. 50.

were observed to have structures reminiscent of ionic crystals, in the sense that there was no preferential association of one structural unit with another. These substances, however, exhibited properties distinctly different from those normally associated with ionic systems. For example, diamond has physical characteristics similar to those of sodium chloride, except that it is composed of the same kind of atom rather than of two or more different kinds. Intuitively, it would be difficult to argue that the diamond structure represents a collection of ions, since this would imply that some of the carbon atoms gained electrons at the expense of other carbon atoms in the same structure. If it is assumed that all carbon atoms are alike, there is no reason to suspect that a given carbon atom would suddenly acquire an electron from an identical neighboring atom. The structure of diamond was determined by W. H. BRAGG and W. L. BRAGG who provided the following description.

▼   "The structure of the cubic crystals which have so far been investigated by these methods may be considered as derived from the face-centred lattice (Figure 8–6): that is to say, the centres which are effective in causing

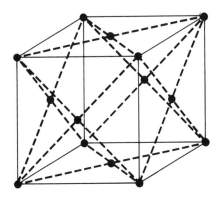

FIGURE 8–6

the reflection of the X-rays are placed one at each corner and one in the middle of each face of the cubical element of volume. This amounts to assigning four molecules to each such cube, for in general one atom in each molecule is so much more effective than the rest that its placing determines the structure from our point of view. There are four, because the eight atoms at the corners of the cube only count as one, each of them belonging equally to eight cubes, and the six atoms in the centres of the faces only count as three, each of them belonging equally to two cubes."[16]

"It is not very easy to picture these dispositions in space. But we have

[16] W. H. BRAGG and W. L. BRAGG, "The Structure of Diamond," *Proceedings of the Royal Society (London)*, **89**, 279 (1913–14).

come to a point where we may readjust our methods of defining the positions of the atoms as we have now placed them, and arrive at a very simple result indeed. Every carbon atom . . . has four neighbours at distances from it equal to 1.522×10^{-8} cm., oriented with respect to it in directions which are parallel to the four diagonals of the cube."[17]

"The appearance of the model when viewed at right angles to a cube diagonal is shown in Figure 8–7. . . . The union of every carbon atom to

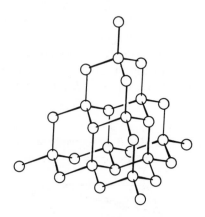

FIGURE 8–7

four neighbours in a perfectly symmetrical way might be expected in view of the persistent tetravalency of carbon. The linking of six carbon atoms into a ring is also an obvious feature of the structure. But it would not be right to lay much stress on these facts at present, since other crystals which do not contain carbon atoms possess, apparently, a similar structure."[18] ▲

It is apparent from the arrangement of the atoms in diamond (Figure 8–7) that each carbon atom is surrounded by four other carbon atoms equidistant from it in a tetrahedral array, and that there are no preferred collections of atoms in this structure which can be interpreted as molecules. In fact, the entire crystal represents a molecule! A similar structure was observed for zinc blende, ZnS (Figure 8–8), in which two different atoms combine to form a giant crystal.

METALS

The metals, e.g. chromium (Figure 8–9), form another class of substances whose crystal structures involve the formation of a regular pattern of the

[17] *Ibid.*, p. 283.
[18] *Ibid.*, p. 283.

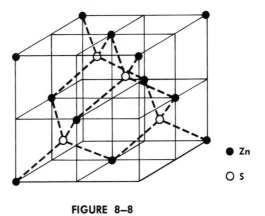

FIGURE 8–8

The crystal structure of zinc blende, ZnS.

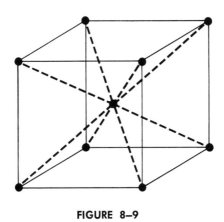

FIGURE 8–9

The body-centered cubic structure of chromium.

same atom. However, the properties of metals are different from those of the other giant molecules. For example, diamond and zinc blende do not conduct electricity as does a metal. Thus the atoms in a metal must be bound together in such a way as to permit the free passage of electrons through the structure. The electrons in diamond, a virtual nonconductor, must be more restrained. The BRAGGS summarized the structural characteristics of metals (and alloys) in the following way.

▼ "Metallic structures are composed of electropositive elements, such as (those which) in ionic compounds part with electrons and became positive ions. A metal may be described as an assemblage of positive ions and free electrons, though such a description carries us little further unless it is based on a theory of the part played by the 'free' electrons in the structure.

In ionic compounds the constituent units are positive and negative, and their relative number is defined by the condition that the total charge should balance; in homopolar compounds directed valencies between atoms exist and the composition is sharply defined. In metals and alloys, on the other hand, the contrasted constituents are the positive ions on one hand and the common electronic structure on the other hand."[19]   ▲

This brief survey of the arrangements of atoms in crystals indicates that several types of associations had to be accounted for by any theory of bonding. It was found that atoms are basically bound together by (a) electrostatic forces as in ionic crystals, or by (b) covalent bonds as in naphthalene, diamond, or the metals. In the latter two instances, the entire crystal must be considered the molecule, and the bonds formed between the atoms are covalent or electron-shared bonds. However, in the case of naphthalene, the atoms within a given molecule are held together by covalent bonds and only weak forces act between the molecules. The structure of ionic substances can be understood by considering the most efficient manner of packing spheres of different sizes carrying opposite charges so that the repulsive forces between all spheres of the same charge are balanced by the attractive forces between all spheres of the opposite charge. The nature of covalent bonds, however, requires a considerably more involved theory.

SUGGESTED READING

Alexander, L. E. "X-rays, Crystals, and Life. Part I," *Chemistry*, **37**, No. 8, 6 (1964); "X-rays, Crystals, and Life. Part II," *Chemistry*, **37**, No. 9, 5 (1964).

Etzel, H. W. "Ionic Crystals," *Journal of Chemical Education*, **38**, 225 (1961).

Fernelius, W. C. "The Nature of the Metallic State," *Journal of Chemical Education*, **12**, 53 (1935).

Gehman, W. G. "Standard Ionic Crystal Structures," *Journal of Chemical Education*, **40**, 54 (1963).

Higgins, M. L. "The Structure of Matter. IV. The Structure of Crystals," *Journal of Chemical Education*, **4**, 73 (1927).

Stillwell, C. W. "Crystal Chemistry," *Journal of Chemical Education*, **13**, 415 (1936).

Verhoek, F. H. "What is a Metal," *Chemistry*, **37**, No. 11, 6 (1964).

Wannier, G. H. "Nature of Solids," *Scientific American*, **187**, No. 6, 39 (1952).

[19] SIR LAWRENCE BRAGG, *The Crystalline State: Volume I. A General Survey* (London: G. Bell and Sons, Ltd., 1949), p. 118.

CHAPTER 9

The Electrical Nature of the Chemical Bond

EARLY SUGGESTIONS

The dualistic theory of Berzelius was discredited in an attempt to apply it to molecular systems, even though it had been used successfully to explain ionic systems; however, a thread of the concept that electrical forces were involved in covalent bonds persisted until Lewis made his definitive statements concerning the nature of the chemical bond. Thus, in 1881, Helmholtz,[1] in his Faraday Lecture, stated:

▼ "I think the facts leave no doubt that the very mightiest among the chemical forces are of electric origin. The atoms cling to their electric charges, and opposite electric charges cling to each other; but I do not suppose that other molecular forces are excluded, working directly from atom to atom. Several of our leading chemists have lately begun to distinguish two classes of compounds, viz., molecular aggregates and typical compounds, the latter being united by atomic affinities, the former not.

"Electrolytes belong to the latter class. If we conclude from the facts that every unit of affinity is charged with one equivalent either of positive or of negative electricity, they can form compounds, being electrically neutral only if every unit charged positively unites under the influence of a mighty electric attraction with another unit charged negatively. You see

---

[1] Hermann Ludwig Ferdinand von Helmholtz (1821–1894): Professor at Königsberg (1849), Bonn (1855), Heidelberg (1858), and Berlin (1871). Helmholtz' early training was in medicine and the first three chairs he occupied were chairs of physiology. Although he contributed to the advancement of medicine, inventing among other things the ophthalmoscope, he is best remembered for his work in physics and mathematics.

that this ought to produce compounds in which every unit of affinity of every atom is connected with one and only one other unit of another atom. This, as you will see immediately, is the modern chemical theory of quantivalence, comprising all the saturated compounds. The fact that even elementary substances, with few exceptions, have molecules composed of two atoms, makes it probable that even in these cases electric neutralisation is produced by the combination of two atoms, each charged with its full electric equivalent, not by neutralisation of every single unit of affinity."[2] ▲

It is interesting to note Helmholtz' suggestion that electrical forces play an important part in the formation of diatomic molecules of elementary substances.

Ramsay,[3] in his presidential address to The Chemical Society in 1908, suggested that electrons can bind atoms together. He considered electrons to be "elements" which could enter into chemical reactions. The argument is best presented in his own words.

▼   "The hypothesis admits of short statement. It is: electrons are atoms of the chemical element, electricity; they possess mass; they form compounds with other elements; they are known in the free state, that is, as molecules; they serve as the 'bonds of union' between atom and atom. The electron may be assigned the symbol 'E.' "[4]

"When the white, opaque, lustrous metal sodium burns in the yellow gas chlorine, small, white, transparent crystals of common salt are produced. These crystals are soluble in water, the solution is also transparent and colourless, and its properties do not materially differ from those of the mean of salt and water. The power possessed by the solution of retarding the passage of light is very nearly proportional to the powers of the salt and the water, taken in the proportion in which they occur in solution. The specific heat of the solution, and many other properties, are also mean properties. What mechanism can we assign to the change which occurs when sodium burns in chlorine? When salt is dissolved in water and a

    [2] H. HELMHOLTZ, "On the Modern Development of Faraday's Concept of Electricity," *Journal of the Chemical Society*, **39**, 301 (1881).
    [3] Sir William Ramsay (1852–1916): Professor of Chemistry at Bristol (1880) and at University College, London (1887). Ramsay received his degree for work on *ortho*-toluic acid and for more than ten years continued to do research in organic chemistry. He then became interested in inorganic chemistry and is best remembered for his discovery of the rare gases. Ramsay won the Nobel Prize in chemistry in 1904 "for the discovery of gaseous, indifferent elements in the air and the determination of their place in the periodic system."
    [4] W. RAMSAY, "The Electron as an Element," *Journal of the Chemical Society*, **93**, 778 (1908).

'current of electricity' is passed through the solution, that is, when two platinum plates, one kept negatively and the other kept positively charged, are dipped into it, sodium travels towards the negative plate, and would, were no secondary action to occur, deposit in its original metallic state; similarly, chlorine would be liberated at the positive plate. We say that the salt is 'ionised in solution,' and we believe that the sodium ion remains an ion because of the positive charge which it carries, and, similarly, the properties of the chlorine ion are due to its negative charge. On removing these charges, the 'elements' as we know them are liberated as such.

"Now, I would argue that in the light of modern knowledge we must suppose that the terms 'positive' and 'negative' mean merely 'minus electrons' and 'plus electrons'; that the sodium ion or 'sodion' is an element; that the metal sodium is a compound of the element 'sodion' with an electron; that the chlorine ion is a compound of an electron (actually of more than one electron; see below) with an atom of chlorine."[5]

"Let us again consider the combination of sodium with chlorine to form common salt. If it be conceded that salt differs from its solution only in so far as the mobility of the solution permits of transfer of ions, the transfer of an electron from the sodium to the chlorine must take place at the moment of combination. Symbolised, if we write E for electron and simplify the reaction, dealing for the moment with an atom and not with a molecule of chlorine, we have

$$ENa + Cl = NaECl.$$

Here the electron serves as the bond of union between the sodium and the chlorine.

"If it be desired to form a mental picture of what occurs, let me suggest a fanciful analogy which may serve the purpose: it is that an electron is an amoeba-like structure, and that ENa may be conceived as an orange of sodium surrounded by a rind of electron; that on combination, the rind separates from the orange and forms a layer or cushion between the Na and the Cl, and that on solution the electron attaches itself to the chlorine in some similar fashion, forming an ion of chlorine. It will be noticed that the E fills the place usually occupied by a bond, thus: Na—Cl. It happens providentially that the bond and the negative sign are practically the same; Na$-$Cl may be supposed to ionise thus: Na($-$Cl), the negative charge or electron remaining with the chlorine.

"Let us next consider a fundamental question, which, however, I do not remember to have seen raised. In ordinary parlance, hydrogen and chlorine are termed monads, and may be represented as each possessing a bond

[5] *Ibid.*, p. 780.

of affinity, thus, H—, Cl—. Now, when they unite, are these two bonds or one? Should we write H—Cl with one bond, or H— —Cl with two? Considering a bond as an electron, the symbol Cl— is wrong for an atom of chlorine; it has, strictly speaking, no bond, that is, no electron, but merely possesses the power of receiving one from the hydrogen."[6]   ▲

It should be noted that Ramsay came close to defining an electron-pair bond when he asked, "Should we write H—Cl with one bond, or H——Cl with two?" Because he did not know the number of valence electrons for each element, he was led to the simplest assumption (which was erroneous), i.e., that only a single electron is required to form a bond. Although Ramsay took a peculiar point of view in his discussion, it is apparent that he thought of electrons as being intimately involved in chemical reactions as well as in the forces which hold compound matter together.

THOMSON'S CHEMICAL BOND

Sir J. J. Thomson's studies on the electrical conductivity of gases indicated that the molecules of elementary gases, e.g., iodine, dissociate into both positive and negative ions when the gas is heated. These observations led to the conclusion "that if the atoms in the molecules of the compound gas are charged, the atoms in the molecules of elementary gases are also charged."[7]

Thomson was the first to suggest a detailed theory which attempted to discuss the manner in which electrical forces hold two atoms together to form a molecule. Although he applied his arguments to an incorrect model of the atom, i.e., the one in which electrons are embedded in a sphere of positive electricity, his suggestions contain the germ of the idea which was adopted later.

▼   "A very important and interesting subject of investigation is the nature of the forces that would be exerted between groups of corpuscles and its application to the theory of chemical combination.

"We shall begin by considering the forces between two groups in some simple cases. Let us begin with the simplest of all when we have a single corpuscle at the centre of a sphere of positive electrification. Let us take two such systems equal in all respects, then as long as one is wholly outside the other there will be neither attraction nor repulsion between the systems; when, however, the spheres cut, as in Figure 9–1, the systems will

---

[6] *Ibid.*, p. 781.
[7] J. J. Thomson, *Corpuscular Theory of Matter* (New York: Charles Scribner's Sons, 1907), p. 31.

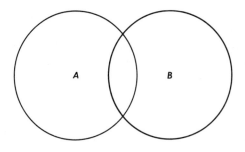

FIGURE 9–1

attract each other. To see this, consider the action of the system A on B; there will be no action on that part of B which is outside A, while the action on the part of the positive electricity of B which is inside A will be an attraction towards the centre of A, for inside a sphere the force due to the negative corpuscle at the centre is greater than that due to the positive electricity. The corpuscles will remain at the centres of their respective spheres until they come so close together that the centre of one sphere lies inside the other sphere; when this stage is reached the corpuscles begin to be displaced and are pushed apart so as to be outside the line joining the two centres. In this case there is no difference in the electrification of the spheres; we cannot say that one is positively the other negatively electrified; and if the spheres were separated after having been together they would each be neutral, the positive electricity in each sphere being balanced by the negative charge at the centre. We thus see that it is possible to have forces electrical in their origin binding the two systems together without a resultant charge on either system. If, however, the spheres were of very different size, then if they were brought close enough together the two corpuscles would go inside one sphere and would remain so after the spheres were pulled apart; thus one sphere would be positively, the other negatively, electrified."[8]   ▲

THOMSON later attempted to describe the electronic concepts of chemical combination more explicitly when he wrote:

▼   "On the view that the attraction between the atoms in a chemical compound is electrical in its origin, the ability of an element to enter into chemical combination depends upon its atom having the power of acquiring a charge of electricity. This, on the preceding view, implies either that the uncharged atom is unstable and has to lose one or more corpuscles before it can get into a steady state, or else that it is so stable that it can

[8] *Ibid.*, p. 120.

retain one or more additional corpuscles without any of the original corpuscles being driven out. If the range of stability is such that the atom, though stable when uncharged, becomes unstable when it receives an additional corpuscle, the atom will not be able to receive a charge either of positive or negative electricity, and will therefore not be able to enter into chemical combination. Such an atom would have the properties of the atoms of such elements as argon or helium.

"The view that the forces which bind together the atoms in the molecules of chemical compounds are electrical in their origin, was first proposed by Berzelius; it was also the view of Davy and of Faraday. Helmholtz, too, declared that the mightiest of the chemical forces are electrical in their origin. Chemists in general seem, however, to have made but little use of this idea, having apparently found the conception of 'bonds of affinity' more fruitful. This doctrine of bonds is, however, when regarded in one aspect almost identical with the electrical theory. The theory of bonds when represented graphically supposes that from each univalent atom a straight line (the symbol of a bond) proceeds; a divalent atom is at the end of two such lines, a trivalent atom at the end of three, and so on; and that when the chemical compound is represented by a graphic formula in this way, each atom must be at the end of the proper number of the lines which represent the bonds. Now, on the electrical view of chemical combination, a univalent atom has one unit charge, if we take as our unit of charge the charge on the corpuscle; the atom is therefore the beginning or end of one unit Faraday tube: the beginning if the charge on the atom is positive, the end if the charge is negative. A divalent atom has two units of charge and therefore it is the origin or termination of two unit Faraday tubes. Thus, if we interpret the 'bond' of the chemist as indicating a unit Faraday tube, connecting charged atoms in the molecule, the structural formulae of the chemist can at once be translated into the electrical theory. There is, however, one point of difference which deserves a little consideration: the symbol indicating a bond on the chemical theory is not regarded as having direction; no difference is made on this theory between one end of a bond and the other. On the electrical theory, however, there is a difference between the ends, as one end corresponds to a positive, the other to a negative charge."[9]   ▲

Thomson's use of the term "Faraday tubes" reflects an attempt to connect atoms physically, presumably because, like Faraday, he did not basically agree with the idea of forces acting at a distance and having no physical connection to their origin. Faraday had suggested the concept of an electric

[9] J. J. THOMSON, *Electricity and Matter* (New York: Charles Scribner's Sons, 1904), pp. 132–134.

field acting through "lines of force" to connect the bodies exerting the forces. THOMSON adopted this concept when he used the term "Faraday tube" in describing the forces which hold molecules together.

▼   "Instead of an intangible action at a distance between two electrified bodies, Faraday regarded the whole space between the bodies as full of stretched mutually repellent springs. The charges of electricity to which alone an interpretation had been given on the fluid theories of electricity were on this view just the ends of these springs, and an electric charge, instead of being a portion of fluid confined to the electrified body, was an extensive arsenal of springs spreading out in all directions to all parts of the field.

"To make our ideas clear on this point let us consider some simple cases from Faraday's point of view. Let us first take the case of two bodies with equal and opposite charges, whose lines of force are shown in Figure 9–2.

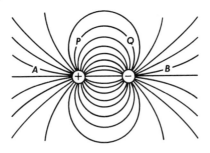

FIGURE 9–2

You notice that the lines of force are most dense along *AB*, the line joining the bodies, and that there are more lines of force on the side of *A* nearest to *B* than on the opposite side. Consider the effect of the lines of force on *A;* the lines are in a state of tension and are pulling away at *A;* as there are more pulling at *A* on the side nearest to *B* than on the opposite side, the pulls on *A* toward *B* overpower those pulling *A* away from *B*, so that *A* will tend to move toward *B;* it was in this way that Faraday pictured to himself the attraction between oppositely electrified bodies. Let us now consider the condition of one of the curved lines of force, such as *PQ;* it is in a state of tension and will therefore tend to straighten itself; how is it prevented from doing this and maintained in equilibrium in a curved position? We can see the reason for this if we remember that the lines of force repel each other and that the lines are more concentrated in the region between *PQ* and *AB* than on the other side of *PQ;* thus the repulsion of the lines inside *PQ* will be greater than the repulsion of those outside and the line *PQ* will be bent outwards.

"Let us now pass from the case of two oppositely electrified bodies to that of two similarly electrified ones, the lines of force for which are shown in Figure 9–3. Let us suppose A and B are positively electrified; since the lines of force start from positively and end on negatively electrified bodies, the lines starting from A and B will travel away to join some body or bodies possessing the negative charges corresponding to the positive ones on A and B; let us suppose that these charges are a considerable distance away, so that the lines of force from A would, if B were not present, spread out, in the part of the field under consideration, uniformly in all directions. Consider now the effect of making the system of lines of force attached to A and B approach each other; since these lines repel each other the lines of force on the side of A nearest B will be pushed to the opposite side of A, so that the lines of force will now be densest on the far side of A; thus the pulls exerted on A in the rear by the lines of force will be greater than those in the front and the result will be that A will be pulled away from B. We notice that the mechanism producing this repulsion is of exactly the same type as that which produced the attraction in the previous case, and we may if we please regard the repulsion between A and B as due to the attractions on A and B of the complementary negative charges which must exist in other parts of the field.

"The results of the repulsion of the lines of force are clearly shown in the case represented in Figure 9–4, that of two oppositely electrified plates; you will notice that the lines of force between the plates are straight except near the edges of the plates; this is what we should expect as the downward pressure exerted by the lines of force above a line in this part of the field will be equal to the upward pressure exerted by those below it. For a line of force near the edge of the plate, however, the pressure of the lines of force below will exceed the pressure from those above, and the line of force will bulge out until its curvature and tension counteract the squeeze from inside; this bulging is very plainly shown in Figure 9–4.

"So far our use of the lines of force has been descriptive rather than

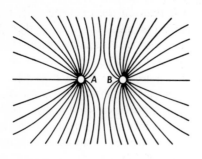

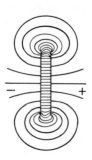

FIGURE 9–3   **FIGURE 9–4**

metrical; it is, however, easy to develop the method so as to make it metrical. We can do this by introducing the idea of *tubes of force*. If through the boundary of any small closed curve in the electric field we draw the lines of force, these lines will form a tubular surface, and if we follow the lines back to the positively electrified surface from which they start and forward on to the negatively electrified surface on which they end, we can prove that the positive charge enclosed by the tube at its origin is equal to the negative charge enclosed by it at its end. By properly choosing the area of the small curve through which we draw the lines of force, we may arrange that the charge enclosed by the tube is equal to the unit charge. Let us call such a tube a Faraday tube — then each unit of positive electricity in the field may be regarded as the origin and each unit of negative electricity as the termination of a Faraday tube. We regard these Faraday tubes as having direction, their direction being the same as that of the electric force, so that the positive direction is from the positive to the negative end of the tube. If we draw any closed surface then the difference between the number of Faraday tubes which pass out of the surface and those which pass in will be equal to the algebraic sum of the charges inside the surface."[10]   ▲

THOMSON then proceeded to apply these ideas to the problem of the chemical bond.

▼   "An example or two may perhaps be the easiest way of indicating the effect of this consideration. Let us take the gas ethane whose structural formula is written

$$
\begin{array}{ccc}
H & & H \\
\diagdown & & \diagup \\
H\!-\!C & \!-\! & C\!-\!H \\
\diagup & & \diagdown \\
H & & H
\end{array}
$$

According to the chemical view there is no difference between the two carbon atoms in this compound; there would, however, be a difference on the electrical view. For let us suppose that the hydrogen atoms are all negatively electrified; the three Faraday tubes going from the hydrogen atoms to each carbon atom give a positive charge of three units on each carbon atom. But in addition to the Faraday tubes coming from the hydrogen atoms, there is one tube which goes from one carbon atom to the other. This means an additional positive charge on one carbon atom and a negative charge on the other. Thus, one of the carbon atoms will have a charge of four positive units, while the other will have a charge of three

[10] *Ibid.*, pp. 10–15.

positive and one negative unit, *i.e.,* two positive units; so that on this view the two carbon atoms are not in the same state."[11]   ▲
_____

About a year after Lewis showed the relationship between the electronic structure of an atom, its position in the periodic chart, and the type of chemical combinations it can undergo, Thomson presented a similar suggestion; he attempted, however, to describe the details of the process by which electrons bind molecules together. The following passage is a concise outline of THOMSON's arguments concerning the source of chemical affinity.

_____

▼   "We regard the negatively electrified corpuscles[12] in an atom as arranged in a series of consecutive layers; those in the inner layers we suppose are so firmly fixed that they do not adjust themselves so as to cause the atom to attract other atoms in its neighbourhood. There may, however, be a ring of corpuscles near the surface of the atom which are mobile and which have to be fixed if the atom is to be saturated. We suppose, moreover, that the number of corpuscles of this kind may be anything from 0 to 8, but that when the number reaches 8 the ring is so stable that the corpuscles are no longer mobile and the atom is so to speak self-saturated.

"The number of these mobile corpuscles in an atom of an element is equal to the number of the group in which the element is placed on Mendeleef's arrangement.

"Thus helium and neon have no free corpuscles; hydrogen, lithium, sodium, potassium, each 1; beryllium, magnesium, calcium and strontium, 2; boron, aluminium, 3; carbon and silicon, 4; nitrogen, phosphorus, and arsenic, 5; oxygen, sulphur, and selenium, 6; fluorine, chlorine, bromine, and iodine, 7.

"Now let us consider how the corpuscles in these atoms can be fixed. They are not fixed when the atom is by itself. In this case the tube of force starting from a corpuscle in the atom, returns to a positive charge in the same atom and possesses considerable mobility, as the corpuscle at one end of it can move freely about in the atom. The corpuscle will not be fixed unless the tube of force at its end is anchored to something not in the atom, i.e. it must end on another atom. Thus if there are *n* free corpuscles in the atom, to fix these and thus saturate the atom, the *n* tubes of force which start from the *n* corpuscles must all end on other atoms and not return to the original atom. Thus to ensure saturation from every free corpuscle in an atom, a tube of force must pass out of that atom and end on some other, and this must hold for every atom in the molecule. When

[11] *Ibid.,* p. 134.
[12] Electrons.

the atoms are electrically neutral, i.e. have no excess of positive over negative charge or *vice-versa,* for each tube of force which passes out of an atom, another must come in; and thus each atom containing n corpuscles must be the origin of n tubes going to other atoms and also the termination of n tubes coming from other atoms.

"Thus consider two atoms A and B each of which contains one free corpuscle, denote these corpuscles by α and β respectively. Then α and β will be fixed if a tube of force goes from α in A to the positive core of B and another from β to the positive core of A: in this case the molecule AB will be saturated. If, however, B had contained two mobile corpuscles β and γ, then, though α might be fixed by a tube going from it to the core of B, yet since only one tube goes out of A only one can come in; thus only the tube from one of the corpuscles in B can go to A; the tube from the other must return to B, and thus this corpuscle will not be fixed and B will not be saturated. If, however, there is a second atom of A in the neighbourhood or any other atom C which contains only one free corpuscle, then this tube of force from γ can go to the positive core of C while the tube from the corpuscle in C comes to the core of B. With this arrangement every mobile corpuscle in the system is anchored by a tube of force to some other atom, and thus deprived of mobility: hence the system will be saturated."[13]   ▲

It is apparent that Thomson was attempting to preserve the mobility of electrons in free atoms and yet use the electric charge of the electron to bind atoms together into compounds. However, in his interpretation of the binding process, the electrons had to be constrained to certain positions within the atom by the "Faraday tubes" of force.

THOMSON then attempted to relate the tubes of force to the lines drawn between atoms.

▼   "We may in a diagram represent the tubes of force proceeding from a corpuscle in an atom by a straight line drawn from the symbol representing the atom, and we see that the condition that all the atoms in the molecule should be saturated is that we should be able to draw a diagram so that the symbol which represents any atom which contains n free corpuscles should be the origin of n of these lines going to the symbols representing other atoms, and the termination of an equal number coming from other atoms.

"If we take the structural formula of any valency compound as represented in the usual way by bonds between the atoms, and double each of

[13] J. J. THOMSON, "The Forces Between Atoms and Chemical Affinity," *Philosophical Magazine* [6], **27,** 781 (1914).

the lines representing a bond, then we may regard one of these lines as representing a tube of force going from the atom and the other a tube entering the atom; and inasmuch as in the diagram of a valency compound the symbol representing an atom of valency n is connected with n of these bonds, we see that the condition given above for saturation will be fulfilled. Thus every compound which satisfied the usual conditions for valency will also satisfy the conditions of our theory."[14]   ▲

A similar idea was presented in more detail by Stark,[15] who considered the valence electrons as attracting simultaneously the positive parts of two different atoms. Thus the electron became the means by which atoms are bound together. Stark described the chemical bond pictorially by drawing lines of force between the positive nuclei and the valence electrons. Figure 9–5 represents the interactions in the ammonia molecule,[16] and Figures 9–6 and 9–7 represent Stark's model for the carbon-carbon and carbon-hydrogen

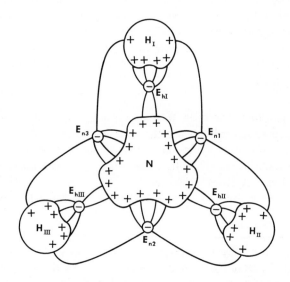

FIGURE 9–5

Stark's model of the ammonia molecule.

[14] *Ibid.,* p. 783.

[15] Johannes Stark (1874–1957): Professor of Physics at Aachen (1909), Griefswald (1917), and Würzberg (1920). He conducted research on the effect of electrical fields on spectral lines and the polarization of light, and demonstrated the Doppler effect for canal rays. Stark was awarded the Nobel Prize for physics in 1919 in recognition of these contributions.

[16] J. Stark, *Prinzipien der Atomdynamik,* Part III (Leipzig: Verlag von S. Hirzel, 1915), p. 99.

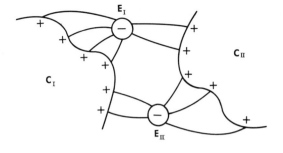

FIGURE 9–6

Stark's model of the carbon-carbon bond.

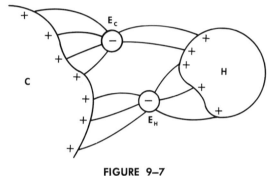

FIGURE 9–7

Stark's model of the carbon-hydrogen bond.

bonds,[17] respectively. It should be noted that, in the latter two representations, Stark shows the presence of two electrons between the two bound atoms.

THE BOHR CONCEPT OF A CHEMICAL BOND

BOHR also considered the binding of two nuclei to occur through the electrical interactions of electrons with nuclei; his arguments proceed as follows:

▼ "According to Rutherford's theory of the structure of atoms, the difference between an atom of an element and a molecule of a chemical combination is that the first consists of a cluster of electrons surrounding a single positive nucleus of exceedingly small dimensions and of a mass great in comparison with that of the electrons, while the latter contains at least two nuclei at distances from each other comparable with the distances apart of the electrons in the surrounding cluster.

[17] *Ibid.,* p. 80.

"The leading idea used in the former papers was that the atoms were formed through the successive binding by the nucleus of a number of electrons initially nearly at rest. Such a conception, however, cannot be utilized in considering the formation of a system containing more than a single nucleus; for in the latter case there will be nothing to keep the nuclei together during the binding of the electrons. In this connexion it may be noticed that while a single nucleus carrying a large positive charge is able to bind a small number of electrons, on the contrary, two nuclei highly charged obviously cannot be kept together by the help of a few electrons. We must therefore assume that configurations containing several nuclei are formed by the interaction of systems — each containing a single nucleus — which already have bound a number of electrons."[18]   ▲

Bohr then goes on to develop mathematically the theory that two positive nuclei can be held together by a ring of electrons rotating around the line connecting the nuclei. This model was adopted later by Kossel, who also attempted to show that chemical bonds arise from a sharing of electrons. It will be recalled that, in Kossel's model of the atom, electrons were distributed in concentric rings, and, according to Kossel, it was these rings of electrons which held molecular species together. The rare gases were given their full complement of eight valence electrons (Figure 9–8, a). The atoms in polar species such as HCl, CaO, or BN also had eight valence electrons associated with them, but the electrons comprising the bonds were distorted more or less towards the more electronegative element (Figure 9–8, b-d). Finally, in nonpolar species such as N_2, the electrons were supposed to be shared equally (Figure 9–8, e). Kossel indicated that ten electrons were shared in the case of N_2, but he put all the electrons in the same ring.

Thus we can conclude that several investigators suggested that covalent compounds are held together by electrical forces. However, it was Lewis and Kossel who showed the relationship between the number of electrons present in the outer shell of an atom and the kinds of compounds which it forms. In the Lewis-Kossel view, the elements reacted to form systems in which each component acquired a more stable arrangement of electrons than either had initially. At that time the rare gases were not known to form compounds, and therefore were considered to have the most stable structures.[19] According to the Lewis-Kossel theory, the nature of the compounds formed de-

---

[18] N. BOHR, "On the Constitution of Atoms and Molecules," *Philosophical Magazine* [6], **26**, 857 (1913).

[19] In 1962 fluorine derivatives of the rare gases were prepared and characterized. Since then a considerable chemistry for these substances has been developed. The Lewis-Kossel arguments are still valid if one considers that an atom with one valence electron (e.g. Na) has a *relatively* less stable electronic structure than if it lost one electron and acquired a rare gas structure. This is not to imply that the rare gas structure could not undergo further reaction — it would merely be more difficult to effect.

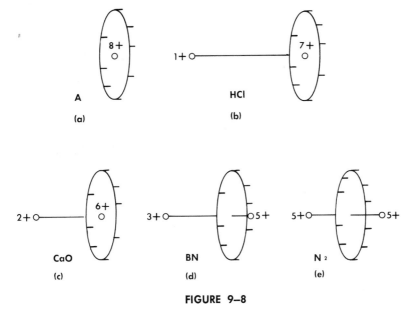

FIGURE 9–8

Kossel's models for some molecular species.

pended upon the relative electronegativity of the combining elements. If atoms with greatly different electronegativities combined, electrons from the less electronegative element would be transferred to the more electronegative element to form an ionic compound. On the other hand, the combination of two elements with nearly equivalent electronegativities would result in the sharing of electrons between the atoms to form molecular species.

It should be noted that neither Lewis nor Kossel attempted to describe the details of the process whereby an electron pair can hold atoms together. Rather, they showed that, by assuming that electrons do indeed behave in this manner, a great deal of chemical knowledge could subsequently be correlated.

SUGGESTED READING

Derjaguin, B. V. "Forces Between Molecules," *Scientific American,* **203,** No. 1, 47 (1960).

Luder, W. F. "Atomic Orbitals and Valence," *Journal of Chemical Education,* **22,** 221 (1945).

Reinmuth, O. "The Structure of Matter," *Journal of Chemical Education,* **5,** 1473 (1928).

Sanderson, R. T. "Principles of Chemical Bonding," *Journal of Chemical Education,* **38,** 382 (1961).

CHAPTER 10

Electron Pairs and Geometry

One of the difficulties in Lewis' original theory of the covalent bond involved the geometrical arrangement of atoms in a molecule. As we have seen, the "ionic bond" is not really a bond in the Lewis sense. Ionic substances can be considered as assemblages of particles, each with a characteristic charge. As Lewis pointed out, the magnitude of the charge for each particular ion is determined by the position of the parent atom in the periodic chart and by the nature of the atom with which it combines. The latter factor determines whether or not an "ionic bond" will be formed, whereas the former factor determines the outer electronic structure of the atoms involved and indicates the number of electrons that will be gained or lost. Thus, the arrangement of ions in a crystalline lattice depends on how efficiently the charged particles can be packed together; the relative sizes and charges of the particles are the important factors for our consideration.

LEWIS AND MOLECULAR GEOMETRY

Lewis' cubical atoms could be easily used to describe the arrangements of atoms in simple molecules such as I_2 (Figure 10–1), in which only one pair of electrons is shared. The theory could also be extended to double bonds, i.e., the sharing of four pairs of electrons by two atoms; Lewis supposed that O_2 and ethylene were molecules in which the bonded atoms shared the faces of a cube (Figure 10–2). Serious difficulties were encountered, however, when the theory was extended to molecules, such as acetylene, in which six electrons are shared by two atoms. It was obvious that a cubical arrangement of electrons could not be used to describe triple bonds. There was no way in which three pairs of electrons could be mutually shared by two atoms and still retain a cubical arrangement. LEWIS realized this difficulty when he wrote the following:

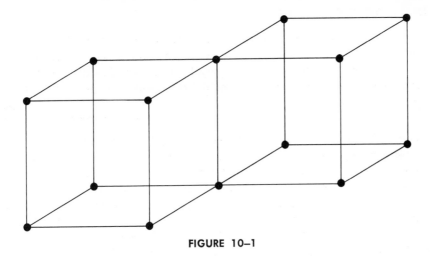

FIGURE 10–1

The Lewis concept of the single electron-pair bond in an I_2 molecule.

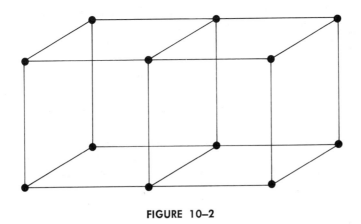

FIGURE 10–2

The Lewis concept of the double electron-pair bond as in, e.g., O_2 and ethylene.

▼ "In my early theory the cube was the fundamental structure of all atomic shells. We have seen, however, in the case of elements with lower atomic weights than lithium, that the *pair* of electrons forms the stable group, and we may question whether in general the pair rather than the group of eight should not be regarded as the fundamental unit. Perhaps the chief reasons for assuming the cubical structure were that this is the most symmetrical arrangement of eight electrons, and is the one in which the electrons are farthest apart. Indeed it seems inherently probable that in elements of large atomic shell (large atomic volume) the electrons are sufficiently far from one another so that Coulomb's law of inverse squares is approximately valid, and in such cases it would seem probable that the mutual repulsion of the eight electrons would force them into the cubical structure."[1]

▲

Lewis changed his point of view concerning the geometry of electronic arrangemênts by considering the distribution of pairs of electrons. His correlations of electron distribution about atoms in molecules with respect to the position of the atoms in the periodic classification indicated that they will achieve a rare gas configuration if possible. Since this configuration can be attained in molecular systems by a sharing of electron pairs, Lewis argued that perhaps the important consideration for the structure of molecules was the distribution of *pairs* of electrons about the atoms. His argument is contained in the following excerpt.

▼   "We are led to assume a somewhat different arrangement of the group of eight electrons, at least in the case of the more nonpolar substances whose molecules are as a rule composed of atoms of small atomic volume.

"The nature of this arrangement is shown in Figure 10–3. The cube representing the electron structure that we have hitherto assumed for the carbon atom is jointed to four other atoms, which are not shown in the figure, but which are attached to the carbon atom each by a pair of electrons. These pairs are indicated by being joined by heavy lines. Assuming now, at least in such very small atoms as that of carbon, that each pair of electrons has a tendency to be drawn together, perhaps by magnetic force if the magneton theory is correct, or perhaps by other forces which become

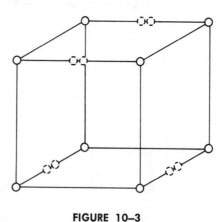

FIGURE 10–3

[1] G. N. LEWIS, "The Atom and the Molecule," *Journal of the American Chemical Society,* **38,** 779 (1916).

appreciable at small distances, to occupy positions indicated by the dotted circles, we then have a model which is admirably suited to portray all of the characteristics of the carbon atom. With the cubical structure it is not only impossible to represent the triple bond, but also to explain the phenomenon of free mobility about a single bond which must always be assumed in stereochemistry. On the other hand, the group of eight electrons in which the *pairs* are symmetrically placed about the center gives identically the model of the tetrahedral carbon atom which has been of such signal utility throughout the whole of organic chemistry."[2]   ▲

It is interesting to note that Lewis was unable to give a rational reason for the pairing of electrons. However, his assumption that four electron pairs will distribute themselves in a tetrahedral arrangement immediately led him to a simpler description of bonding.

▼   "As usual, two tetrahedra, attached by one, two or three corners of each, represent respectively the single, the double and the triple bond. In the first case one pair of electrons is held in common by the two atoms, in the second case two such pairs, in the third case three pairs.

"The triple bond represents the highest possible degree of union between two atoms. Like a double bond it may break one bond, producing two *odd* carbon atoms, but it may also break in a way in which the double bond cannot, to leave a single bond and two carbon atoms (bivalent), each of which has a pair of electrons which is not bound to any other atom.

"The instability of multiple bonds, as well as the general phenomenon of ring formation in organic compounds is admirably interpreted by the Strain Theory of Baeyer. This theory may, however, be put into a far more general form if we make the simple assumption that *all atomic kernels repel one another,* and that molecules are held together only by the pairs of electrons which are held jointly by the component atoms. Thus two carbon atoms with a single bond strive to keep their kernels as far apart as possible, and this condition is met when the adjoining corners of the two tetrahedra lie in the line joining the centers of the tetrahedra. This is an essential element of Baeyer's theory of ring formation. When a single bond changes to a multiple bond and the two atomic shells have two pairs of electrons in common, the kernels are forced nearer together and the mutual repulsion of these kernels greatly weakens the constraints at the points of junction. This diminution in constraint therefore produces a remarkable effect in increasing the mobility of the electrons. In any part of a carbon chain where a number of consecutive atoms are doubly bound there is in that whole portion of the molecule an extraordinary reactivity and freedom of rearrangement. This freedom usually terminates at that

[2] *Ibid.,* p. 780.

point in the chain where an atom has only single bonds and in which there-fore the electrons are held by more rigid constraints, although it must be observed that an increased mobility of electrons (and therefore increased polarity) in one part of the molecule always produces some increase in mobility in the neighboring parts."[3]   ▲

Thus, Lewis states explicitly that bond formation occurs because the at-traction between the electron pairs and the positively charged atomic kernels overcomes the repulsion between two positively charged bodies. A molecular aggregation can be considered analogous to the aggregation of charged par-ticles in a crystalline lattice; viewed in this manner, the positive species (atomic kernels) would be distributed as far apart as possible, but they would also be close to the negative species (electron pairs). However, the question of why electrons pair remains unanswered.

The Expanded Octet

A second difficulty in Lewis' original theory arose from the observation that in many cases atoms could apparently acquire more than an octet of electrons. The Lewis formulation for silicon tetrafluoride, SiF_4, is

$$
\begin{array}{c}
\overset{\cdot\cdot}{:F:} \\[2pt]
\overset{\cdot\cdot}{:F:}\overset{\cdot\cdot}{Si}\overset{\cdot\cdot}{:F:} \\[2pt]
\overset{\cdot\cdot}{:F:} \\[2pt]
\cdot\cdot
\end{array}
$$

but it was known that SiF_4 can react further to form species such as $SiF_6^=$. If each fluorine is attached to the silicon atom by an electron-pair bond, the silicon atom must acquire a share in twelve electrons, rather than eight as Lewis originally suggested. Similar statements can be made concerning the central atom in species such as PF_6^- and SF_6. It rapidly became apparent that Lewis' octet theory was, in fact, a part of a more general theory. Many examples of compounds in which atoms have more than four groups attached to them were known at the time Lewis defined the electron-pair bond. In addition to the systems just mentioned, "complex compounds" were known whose structures had been elucidated by Werner.[4] As an example, the follow-

---

[3] *Ibid.*, p. 780.

[4] Alfred Werner (1866–1919): Professor of Chemistry at Zürich. Werner's most im-portant contribution to chemistry was his theory of valency and the structure of coor-dination compounds. In 1913 he won the Nobel Prize in chemistry for the "recognition of his work on the linkage of atoms in molecules, by which he has thrown fresh light on old problems and opened up new fields of research, particularly in inorganic chem-istry."

ing series of compounds containing platinum, ammonia, and chlorine can be
prepared:

$$PtCl_4 \cdot 6NH_3$$
$$PtCl_4 \cdot 5NH_3$$
$$PtCl_4 \cdot 4NH_3$$
$$PtCl_4 \cdot 3NH_3$$
$$PtCl_4 \cdot NH_3 \cdot KCl$$
$$PtCl_4 \cdot 2KCl$$

Written in this way, these compounds appear to be combinations of platinic
chloride and ammonia, platinic chloride, ammonia, and potassium chloride,
and platinic chloride and potassium chloride. Or, stated in different words,
these compounds appeared to be combinations of substances whose valences
were already satisfied, hence the name "complex compounds."

A study of the properties of these complex compounds led to the conclusion that they could not be described as simple combinations containing individual chemical species. Chemical evidence suggested that these platinum
compounds are best formulated as

$$[Pt(NH_3)_6]Cl_4$$
$$[Pt(NH_3)_5Cl]Cl_3$$
$$[Pt(NH_3)_4Cl_2]Cl_2$$
$$[Pt(NH_3)_3Cl_3]Cl$$
$$[Pt(NH_3)Cl_5]K$$
$$[PtCl_6]K_2$$

where square brackets enclose that portion of the molecule which is not
ionized. A perusal of the species within the brackets indicates that, in each
instance, platinum is associated with six other groups. The species appear to
be related to each other by replacement of an ammonia molecule by a chloride
ion. A similar phenomenon had been observed by Kekulé, who noted that
carbon can be bound to a maximum of four monovalent groups. Perhaps the
questions of why six groups should be attached to a platinum atom and how
a neutral molecule like ammonia could be involved in bond formation were
just as puzzling to Lewis as the tetravalency of carbon had been to Kekulé.

THE COORDINATE COVALENT BOND

Sidgwick[5] suggested that the bond formed between the neutral species and
the metal ion in complex compounds, i.e., between ammonia and platinum,

[5] Nevil Vincent Sidgwick (1863–1952): Professor of Chemistry at Oxford University.
Sidgwick began his career as an organic chemist, but about 1920 he became interested
in the periodic classification of the elements based on the constitution of the atom. The
remainder of his studies were devoted to properties directly dependent on the nature of
the chemical bond such as atomic radii, dipole moments, bond strengths, valency
angles, and molecular configurations.

was similar to that postulated by Lewis to exist between ammonia and the proton in NH_4^+ (see page 115). That is, both of the electrons which form the bond come from one of the atoms, rather than one electron coming from each atom as in the usual covalent bond. This type of bond is called a co-ordinate covalent bond to distinguish it from the common covalent bond. It should be emphasized that the coordinate covalent bond is still a *covalent* bond. The adjective "coordinate" indicates that both of the electrons forming the bond come from one atom. SIDGWICK'S argument is presented in his own words.

▼   "The attachment of a univalent radical like chlorine or NO_2 is a cova-lency of the normal type, to which the radical in question supplies one electron, and the central atom the other. But an independent molecule like water or ammonia must already have an even number of valency electrons, and so cannot form its linkage in this way: if it had a single odd electron available for the purpose, or if it could accommodate one further electron borrowed from the central atom, it would not be able to exist by itself; it must attach itself by sharing with the central atom a lone pair of its own electrons — in other words, by forming a co-ordinate link. All the mole-cules capable of entering into a complex in this way can be shown to have the necessary lone pair: the nitrogen in ammonia has one such pair, and the oxygen in water has two. Thus the number of shared electrons in the valency group of the central atom will be the same whether the co-ordi-nated units are molecules or univalent radicals, and this explains why those of one kind can replace those of the other unit by unit, as they are found to do.

"The characteristic change of electrovalency which accompanies such a replacement necessarily follows. Suppose we start with the non-ionized compound $[Pt(NH_3)_2Cl_4]^0$. If a (neutral) chlorine atom is removed, it will take with it one of the electrons which it previously shared with the platinum, but will leave the other behind. If now an ammonia molecule takes its place, this provides the two electrons required for its attachment, so that the platinum has gained one electron by the exchange. Since it must in the original compound have had the number of electrons required for stability, it now has one too many: it will lose this, and thereby acquire a positive charge, appearing as a cation in the salt $[Pt(NH_3)_3Cl_3]Cl$. The process can be represented by the scheme:

$$[Pt \overset{x}{\text{.}} Cl]^0 \rightarrow [Pt^x]^0 \rightarrow [\underset{x}{Pt} : NH_3]^0 \rightarrow [Pt : NH_3]^+$$

"This change of electrovalency on replacement is not peculiar to the Wernerian complexes. There is a very familiar example in organic chem-istry, though it is not usually formulated in this way. When ammonia acts on methyl chloride, methylamine hydrochloride is formed: the chlorine is replaced by NH_3, and the electrovalency of the complex changes from zero to $+1$:[6]

$$\begin{bmatrix} H & \quad & H \\ & C & \\ H & \quad & Cl \end{bmatrix} + NH_3 = \begin{bmatrix} H & \quad & H \\ & C & \\ H & \quad & NH_3 \end{bmatrix} Cl$$

▲

The Effective Atomic Number

According to Sidgwick's theory of complex compounds, and to Lewis' octet theory, the metal atom attempts to acquire a rare gas configuration. However, in this type of compound the metal ion is numerically further from a rare gas structure and hence must acquire a share in a greater number of electrons. Sidgwick suggested that the formulas of complex compounds could be understood in terms of the total number of electrons about the metal atom, whether or not they are shared. This number of electrons was defined as the "effective atomic number" (E.A.N.), and it was shown that the effective atomic number of the central atom in the majority of complex compounds was equal to the atomic number of the next rare gas. SIDGWICK's description of this concept follows:

▼   "The first step is to determine how many electrons surround the nucleus of an atom in a molecule of known structure, and how many of these are shared with other atoms. As the number in a neutral isolated atom is the atomic number, that in the combined atom (which will obviously vary with the state of combination) may be called the Effective Atomic Number (E.A.N.). The simple rules for determining this may be repeated. We have to find how the original atomic number of the atom in question is modified by the state of combination. We must therefore make the following changes in it.

"(1) For every covalency, due to the attachment of a univalent radical, we add 1.

"(2) For every co-ordinate valency, such as is formed by attaching to the atom a complete molecule, when the atom acts as acceptor, we add 2: when it acts as donor, no change is made.

"(3) If the resulting complex is an ion, we add the value of its negative or subtract that of its positive electrovalency.

[6] N. V. SIDGWICK, *Electronic Theory of Valency* (London: Oxford University Press, 1927), p. 113.

"These are the only rules. The following examples will make their application clear.

B in $K[BF_4]$	$5 + 4 + 1$	$= 10_4$
C in CH_4	$6 + 4$	$= 10_4$
N in NH_3	$7 + 3$	$= 10_3$
N in $[NH_4]Cl$	$7 + 4 - 1$	$= 10_4$

$$\text{Cl in } H \begin{bmatrix} O & & O \\ & \diagdown \text{Cl} \diagup & \\ O & & O \end{bmatrix} \qquad 17 + 1 \qquad\qquad = 18_4$$

Co in $K[Co(NH_3)_2Cl_4]$	$27 + 2 \times 2 + 4 + 1$	$= 36_6$
Co in $[Co(NH_3)_5Cl]Cl_2$	$27 + 2 \times 5 + 1 - 2$	$= 36_6$

"The subscript number following the E.A.N. gives the number of covalent links formed by the atom. This being the number of pairs of shared electrons, the number of unshared is the E.A.N. minus twice the covalency: e.g., for 36_6 it is $36 - 2 \times 6 = 24$."[7]   ▲

Thus, by a simple extension of the Lewis theory, Sidgwick was able to correlate the constitution of many compounds which could not be previously accommodated. In Sidgwick's view, $SiF_4^=$, PF_6^-, and SF_6 had similar electronic structures since they all had the same effective atomic number, i.e., that of the next rare gas, argon; the difference in the formal charges on these species was regarded as a reflection of the position of the central atom in the periodic table. In spite of the success of these ideas, the question of the nature of the covalent link was still unknown, or as SIDGWICK put it,

▼   "We know that the shared electrons enter in some way into the constitution of both the atoms concerned, but we cannot calculate their orbits, or the relations of these to the orbits of the unshared electrons. The mathematical difficulties of this problem are so great that it is unlikely that the physicist will be able to make any great progress with it, unless the chemists to some extent prepare the ground, and by examining the great mass of chemical evidence which they have collected, discover empirically so far as they can what arrangements of shared and unshared electrons do actually occur in stable molecules."[7]   ▲

The Stereochemistry of Electron Pairs

Werner showed, using chemical methods, that the six groups attached to the central atom in complex compounds were situated at the corners of an

[7] *Ibid.*, p. 163.

octahedron. As the physical methods for directly determining the positions of atoms with respect to each other in complex structures were refined and the structures of more and more molecules were elucidated, it became apparent that Werner's structure was correct. Moreover, a thread of continuity began to emerge with respect to the geometries exhibited by compounds. In 1940, SIDGWICK and POWELL pointed out that the arrangement of electron pairs about an atom is related to the number of electrons present, irrespective of whether the electron pairs are shared or unshared.

▼   "If we compare the stereochemical type with the size of the valency group as a whole, and assume that the electron pairs occupy much the same positions whether they are shared or not, it is seen that this size is closely related to, and in most cases uniquely determines, the type of spatial arrangement adopted, and in the following way.

"With a quartet of electrons, the molecule is linear (as in Cl—Hg—Cl).

"With a sextet, the arrangement is planar, and the valency angles 120°, giving with a covalency of 3 the plane symmetrical molecule (as in BF_3) and where it is 2-covalent, as in $SnCl_2$, a triangular molecule.

"With an octet there appear to be two different types, the tetrahedron and the plane square form. All the 2- and 3-covalent octets are derived from the tetrahedron, the 2-covalent being triangular and the 3-covalent pyramidal. The 4-covalent (fully shared) octet is tetrahedral when the electron group (n) preceding the valency octet contains 2, 8, or 18 electrons, and also in the earlier transitional elements when n is not much more than 8. When n is not much less than 18 the planar form appears, while for intermediate values both types occur. The planar form may really be a 4-covalent duodecet, as in the $[ICl_4]^-$ ion (below), which would become possible when n is not less than 12.

"The decet when fully shared (5-covalent) gives the trigonal pyramid. The 4-covalent decet seems to have two forms: (1) a plane square structure in thallous and plumbous compounds (involving a change in the disposition of the 10 electrons), and perhaps (2) in tellurium tetrachloride a distorted tetrahedron, which would naturally arise from the bipyramid by the removal of one of the attached atoms. The 2-covalent decet is found in the trihalide ions such as $[I_3]^-$, which have been shown to be linear, as if derived from the trigonal bipyramid by removing all three equatorial groups.

"The duodecet when fully shared (6-covalent) is octahedral. The 5-covalent form occurs in IF_5, but its structure is not known; the 4-covalent form is that of iodine in the anion $[ICl_4]^-$, which has been shown to be square, and so to be derived from the octahedron by the removal of two trans-groups; the same structure may occur in the planar 4-covalent compounds of the later transitional elements.

"The 14-group occurs in two 7-covalent forms derived respectively from the octahedron and from the trigonal prism by the insertion of a seventh valency.

"Of the 16-group (8-covalent) only one example has been examined, which is found to be dodecahedral."[8]   ▲

_____

These ideas were recently extended to more complex systems by Gillespie[9] and Nyholm[10]; their results are given in Table 10–1 and the corresponding geometrical arrangements are shown in Figure 10–4 (page 158). In fact, the same arguments can be used to determine the shapes of molecules containing double and triple bonds if the electrons in any one bond are treated as a group (Table 10–2, page 159).

The variety of structures that had been precisely determined permitted more detailed explanations to be presented concerning the slight variations from the theoretically ideal structure. GILLESPIE'S and NYHOLM'S arguments follow:

_____

▼   "This simple theory can be considerably improved qualitatively by assuming that electrostatic repulsions between the electron pairs in a valency shell decrease in the order: lone-pair — lone-pair > lone-pair — bond-pair > bond-pair — bond-pair. This can be understood by picturing the lone pairs as being closer to the nucleus than the bonding pairs, which may be imagined pulled out to some extent by the other nucleus with which they are forming a bond. Thus the lone pairs will be closer to each other than the bonding pairs and so will repel each other more strongly. This assumption enables one to give a qualitatively correct account of the decrease of the bond angles in a series such as methane, ammonia, and water and to understand better the shapes of those molecules that could not be predicted unambiguously in Table 10–1.

"On passing from methane to ammonia, we replace a bonding pair by a lone pair, which repels the remaining three bond pairs somewhat more than the original bond pair, so causing the bond angle to decrease from the tetrahedral value of 109° 28'. On passing from ammonia to water we replace another bond pair by a lone pair and the bond angle decreases further.

_____

[8] N. V. SIDGWICK and H. M. POWELL, "Stereochemical Types and Valency Groups," _Proceedings of the Royal Society,_ **176A**, 164 (1940).

[9] Ronald J. Gillespie (1924–   ): Professor of Chemistry at McMaster University, Canada. Gillespie had been interested in molecular structure and the nature of species dissolved in extremely acidic solvents.

[10] Ronald S. Nyholm (1917–   ): Professor of Chemistry at University College, London. Nyholm's research interests have centered in inorganic and physical chemistry with special emphasis on the study of structure and properties of inorganic complex compounds, their magnetic properties, and the stabilization of unusual oxidation states of the metals.

TABLE 10–1

*The Arrangements of Electron Pairs in Valency Shells and the
Shapes of Molecules (Non-transitional Elements)* *

Total no. of electron pairs in valency shell	Arrangement of electron pairs	No. of bonding pairs	No. of non-bonding (lone) pairs	Shape of molecule	Examples
2	Linear	2	0	Linear	$HgCl_2 [Ag(CN)_2]^-$
3	Triangular-plane	3	0	Triangular-plane	BCl_3
		2	1	V-shape	$SnCl_2$ (gas)
4	Tetrahedron	4	0	Tetrahedron	CH_4
		3	1	Trigonal-pyramid	NH_3
		2	2	V-shape	H_2O F_2O
5	Trigonal-bipyramid	5	0	Trigonal-bipyramid	PCl_5
		4	1	Irregular tetrahedron	$TeCl_4$
		3	2	T-shape	ClF_3
		2	3	Linear	$[ICl_2]^-$
6	Octahedron	6	0	Octahedron	SF_6 $[PCl_6]^-$
		5	1	Square-pyramid	IF_5
		4	2	Square	$[ICl_4]^-$
7	Pentagonal-bipyramid	7	0	Pentagonal-bipyramid	IF_7
		6	1	Irregular octahedron	$[SbBr_6]^{3-}$

* Adapted from R. J. Gillespie and R. S. Nyholm, "Inorganic Stereochemistry,"
Quarterly Reviews, **11**, 344 (1951).

"The variations in the bond angle in series of related molecules can be
satisfactorily interpreted by a slight extension of these ideas. Thus, in the
following two series of molecules, the bond angles decrease: NH_3 106° 45′,
PH_3 93° 50′, AsH_3 91° 35′, SbH_3 91° 30′; and H_2O 104° 27′, H_2S 92° 20′.
This can be attributed to the decreasing electronegativity of the central
atom in both series, which allows the bonding pairs to be drawn further

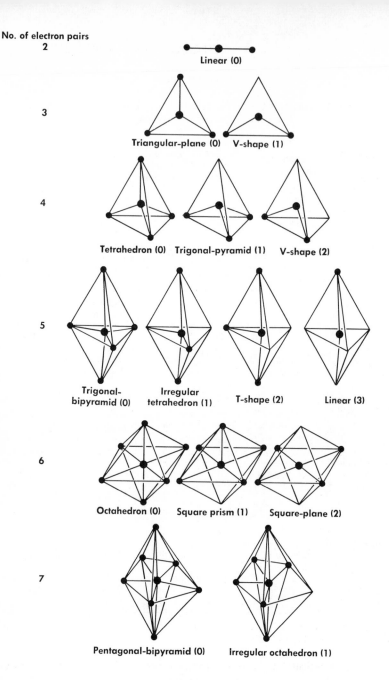

No. of electron pairs

2

Linear (0)

3

Triangular-plane (0)   V-shape (1)

4

Tetrahedron (0)   Trigonal-pyramid (1)   V-shape (2)

5

Trigonal-bipyramid (0)   Irregular tetrahedron (1)   T-shape (2)   Linear (3)

6

Octahedron (0)   Square prism (1)   Square-plane (2)

7

Pentagonal-bipyramid (0)   Irregular octahedron (1)

FIGURE 10–4

*Shapes of molecules (non-transitional elements). The numeral in parentheses is the number of lone pairs of electrons. (Adapted from R. J. Gillespie and R. S. Nyholm, Quarterly Reviews, **11**, 344 (1951).)*

TABLE 10–2

*The Shapes of Molecules Containing Double Bonds**

Total no. of bonds and lone pairs	Arrangement	No. of bonds	No. of lone pairs	Shape of molecule	Examples
2	Linear	2	0	Linear	O:C:O H·C:N
3	Triangular	3	0	Triangular-plane	(structures)
	Plane	2	1	V-shape	(structures)
4	Tetrahedral	4	0	Tetrahedral	(structures)
		3	1	Triangular-pyramid	(structures)
		2	2	V-shape	(structures)
5	Trigonal	5	0	Trigonal-bipyramid	(structures)
		4	1	Irregular tetrahedron	(structures)
6	Octahedron	6	0	Octahedron	(structures)

*Adapted from **R. J. Gillespie** and **R. S. Nyholm**, "Inorganic Stereochemistry," *Quarterly Reviews*, **11**, 345 (1951).

away from the central nucleus by the hydrogen atoms, thereby increasing their distance apart and decreasing the repulsions between them."[11]   ▲

Thus, the simple electrostatic picture of the electron pairs about an atom repelling each other can be used to predict correctly the orientation of the atoms in a molecule. It should be noted that many years earlier Thomson predicted a similar arrangement of electrons in uncombined atoms when he attempted to describe the position of the valence electrons relative to each other. The important point in THOMSON'S arguments and his results are as follows:

▼   "Confining ourselves then to the consideration of things whose existence has been demonstrated we regard the atom as made up of a massive positively electrified centre surrounded by electrons. The number of electrons increasing from one in the atom of hydrogen to a hundred or more in the heavier elements. The positive charge of the centre and the negative charges on the electrons will produce a field of electrical force which will be determinable when the position of the electrons can be specified. Thus the force exerted by the atom and therefore its chemical properties will depend upon the configuration of the electrons and to determine this is one of the most important problems in the electron theory of chemistry.

"This problem is that of determining the way the electrons will arrange themselves under the action of their mutual repulsions and the forces exerted upon them by the positive charge.

"I have therefore adopted the plan of supposing that the law of force between the positive part and the electrons is, at the distances with which we have to deal in the atom, not strictly that of the inverse square, but a more complex one which changes from attraction to repulsion as the distance between the positive charge and the electron diminishes. This hypothesis leads to a simple mental picture of the structure of the atom and its consequences are in close agreement with the facts of chemistry. I suppose that the repulsive force between two *electrons* is always inversely proportional to the square of the distance. With regard to this point I may point out that we have no direct evidence as to what may be the law of force between electrical charges at distances comparable to 10^{-8} cm., which is a distance which we have reason to believe is comparable with that which separates the positive charge from the electron in the atom. The direct experimental verification of this law has been of course made at incomparably greater distances, while the direct experiments, such as those on the scattering of the alpha particles, only give information as to the law at distances very small compared with 10^{-8} cm.

[11] R. J. GILLESPIE and R. S. NYHOLM, "Inorganic Stereochemistry," *Quarterly Reviews,* **11,** 341 (1951).

"I shall assume that the law of force between a positive charge and an electron is expressed by the equation

$$F = \frac{Ee}{r^2} \left(1 - \frac{c}{r}\right) \qquad (1)$$

where F is the attraction between the charges, E, e, the positive and negative charges on the core and electrons, respectively, r the distance between them and c is a constant varying from one kind of atom to another, it is the distance at which the force changes from attraction to repulsion and is of the order of 10^{-8} cm.

"If the law of force is that just given, then a number of electrons can be in stable equilibrium around a positive charge without necessarily describing orbits around it.

ONE ELECTRON ATOM

"Thus, for example, if there is one electron it will be in stable equilibrium at a distance c_1 from the positive charge.

TWO ELECTRON ATOM

"If there are two electrons they will be in equilibrium with the positive charge midway between them; r the distance of either electron from the positive charge is given by the equation

$$\frac{Ee}{r^2} \left(1 - \frac{c_2}{r}\right) = \frac{e^2}{4r^2} \qquad (2)$$

When the positive charge and the two electrons form an electrically neutral system $E = 2e$, so that $c_2/r = 7/8$ or $r = 1.14\ c_2$.

THREE ELECTRON ATOM

"When there are three electrons, they will be in equilibrium at the corners of an equilateral triangle with the positive charge at the centre. r, the distance of any electron from the centre, is given by the equation

$$\frac{Ee}{r^2} \left(1 - \frac{c_3}{r}\right) = \frac{2e^2}{3r^2} \cos 30 \qquad (3)$$

"When the system is electrically neutral $E = 3e$, so that $r = 1.24\ c_3$.

FOUR ELECTRON ATOM

"The most symmetrical arrangement of four electrons is when they are at the corners of a regular tetrahedron. The distance of the electrons from the centre when the atom is neutral is equal to 1.29 c_4. The tetrahedron may be regarded as the ends of two equal lines at right angles to each other and also to the line joining their middle points.

FIVE ELECTRON ATOM

"Five electrons are in equilibrium when arranged so that three are at the corners of an equilateral triangle, the other two at the ends of a line passing through the centre of the triangle and at right angles to its plane; the line is bisected by the plane of the triangle. The distance of the electrons in the triangle from the centre is 1.34 c_5, that of the other two 1.37 c_5.

SIX ELECTRON ATOM

"Six electrons are in equilibrium when at the corners of a regular octahedron. For some purposes it is convenient to regard the octahedron as two equilateral triangles at right angles to the line joining their centres, one triangle being twisted relatively to the other so that the projection of their corners on a parallel plane forms a regular hexagon. The distance of the electrons from the centre is 1.38 c_6.

SEVEN ELECTRON ATOM

"Seven electrons arrange themselves so that five are at the corners of a regular pentagon while the two others are at the ends of a line through the centre at right angles to the plane of the pentagon and which is bisected by that plane. The distance of the electrons in the pentagon from the centre is 1.4 c_7, that of the other two 1.37 c_7.

EIGHT ELECTRON ATOM

"Eight electrons arrange themselves at the corners of a twisted cube, a figure obtained by taking two squares, placing them parallel to each other and at right angles to the line joining their centres, and twisting them relatively to each other so that the projection of their corners on a parallel plane forms a regular octagon."[12]   ▲

---

[12] J. J. THOMSON, "The Electron in Chemistry," *Franklin Institute Journal,* **195,** 596 (1923).

Thomson's results agree with those of the Sidgwick-Powell-Gillespie-Nyholm system if the word "pair" is inserted after the numbers "one," "two," "three," etc., in the quotation. Had Thomson been speaking of electron pairs, the stereochemical relationships of compounds would probably have been elucidated earlier.

SUGGESTED READING

DeVries, J. "Molecular Structure and Valence," *Journal of Chemical Education,* **13,** 320 (1936).

Fowles, G. W. A. "Lone Pair Electrons," *Journal of Chemical Education,* **34,** 187 (1957).

Gillespie, R. J. "The Valence-Shell Electron-Pair Repulsion (VSEPR) Theory of Directed Valency," *Journal of Chemical Education,* **40,** 295 (1963).

Jones, H. R. "Molecular Shapes and the Balloon Analogy," *Education in Chemistry,* **2,** 25 (1965).

King, L. C. "Molecular Architecture," *Chemistry,* **37,** No. 2, 12 (1964).

Luder, W. F. "Atomic Orbitals and Valence," *Journal of Chemical Education,* **22,** 221 (1945).

Strong, L. E. "Facts, Students, and Ideas," *Journal of Chemical Education,* **39,** 126 (1962).

CHAPTER 11

Electrons and Waves

At this point in our story it should be apparent that a fundamental difference of opinion existed between physicists and chemists. Bohr's picture of the atom, i.e., of electrons moving in discrete circular or elliptical orbits about the nucleus, predicted many of the properties later observed for atoms. Although this model worked very well for "one-electron atoms," it could not be adapted satisfactorily to atoms containing many electrons, and unfortunately it was the latter kind in which chemists were most interested. Chemists could see a relationship between the electronic configuration of atoms and the types of compounds which they formed. However, in attempting to envision the formation of electron-pair bonds between atoms whose electrons revolved about the nucleus, they realized that Bohr's model could never lead to the geometric arrangements known to exist, for example, in carbon compounds. Thus, the chemist, from an experimental point of view, regarded atoms as static systems, while the physicist regarded them as dynamic systems. As LEWIS succinctly put the argument,

▼ "These two views seemed to be quite incompatible, although it is the same atom that is being investigated by chemist and by physicist. If the electrons are to be regarded as taking an essential part in the process of binding atom to atom in the molecule, it seemed impossible that they could be actuated by the simple laws of force, and travelling in the orbits, required by the planetary theory. The permanence of atomic arrangements, even in very complex molecules, is one of the most striking of chemical phenomena. Isomers maintain their identity for years, often without the slightest appreciable transformation. An organic molecule treated with powerful reagents often suffers radical change in one part of the molecule while the remainder appears to suffer no change. It appears inconceivable that these permanent though essentially unstable configurations could result from the simple law of force embodied in Coulomb's law."[1]   ▲

Lewis did not object to electron motion "so long as the electron as a whole is regarded as occupying a fixed position in the atom[2] . . . . for that state of motion which produces no physical effect whatsoever may better be called a state of rest."[3] There were, of course, objections to Lewis' concept of a static atom because it violated the classical laws of electrodynamics. However, the Bohr-Sommerfeld model of the hydrogen atom had been successful precisely because it violated these laws in a certain manner. LEWIS defended his static model from this type of attack in the following words:

▼   "It is to be remarked that while it seems natural to use the same law of force between two charged parts of an atom which is found to hold between two large charged bodies at greater distances from one another, our satisfaction in the success of this experiment is somewhat diminished by the introduction of another assumption which limits the validity of Coulomb's law to certain specific orbits. This is especially true since no suggestion has yet been made regarding the quantitative or even the qualitative laws governing the electron between any two orbits. Indeed the combination of the quantum theory with the Rutherford theory of the atom seems to result in a model which has properties in some sense intermediate between those of an atom whose parts are in rapid motion and those of a static atom."[4]   ▲

He concluded that

▼   ". . . it is the orbit as a whole rather than the particular position of the electron within the orbit that is the thing of essential interest in the Bohr theory. If these orbits are in fixed positions and orientations they may be used as the building stones of an atom which has an essentially static character."[5]   ▲

[1] G. N. LEWIS, *Valence and the Structure of Atoms and Molecules* (New York: The Chemical Catalog Company, Inc., 1923), p. 55.
[2] *Ibid.*, p. 56.
[3] G. N. LEWIS, "The Atom and the Molecule," *Journal of the American Chemical Society,* **38,** 773 (1916).
[4] G. N. LEWIS, *Valence and the Structure of Atoms and Molecules* (New York: The Chemical Catalog Company, Inc., 1923), p. 50.
[5] *Ibid.*, p. 56.

Thus Lewis in his genius anticipated the developments which were to come in the theory of atomic and molecular structure.

ELECTRONIC WAVES

The basic difficulty which beset the Bohr-Sommerfeld atom lay in treating the electron as a discrete particle travelling along a predictable path, much as a billiard ball moves along a table top. The key to solving the dilemma posed by Lewis was supplied in 1924 by Louis de Broglie,[6] who proposed that electrons have a dual nature. This suggestion can be considered as an extension of the quantum theory as applied to electromagnetic radiation.

Certain experiments (diffraction) can be performed with light which suggest that it consists of electromagnetic waves. However, other experiments (for example, the photoelectric effect) are best interpreted on the assumption that light consists of particles known as photons. Einstein[7] expressed the relationship, shown in Equation 1, between the energy, E, of a photon and

$$E = h\nu \tag{1}$$

the frequency, ν, of the radiation associated with it where h is Planck's constant, a fundamental constant of nature. The energy of a moving particle is dependent on its mass and velocity, as shown by Equation 2, which gives the energy for a photon of mass, m, moving at the velocity of light, c.

$$E = mc^2 \tag{2}$$

De Broglie suggested that, just as light can have a dual nature, electrons (as well as other elementary particles) can also have a dual nature. Combining Equations 1 and 2 gives

$$\frac{h\nu}{c} = mc \tag{3}$$

But, since the frequency of the radiation and its wavelength are related by $\lambda = c/\nu$, Equation 3 becomes

[6] Prince Louis Victor de Broglie (1892–   ): Member of an illustrious old French family. De Broglie received the Nobel Prize in physics in 1922 "for his discovery of the wave character of electrons."

[7] Albert Einstein (1879–1955): Professor of Physics at the Universities of Zürich, Prague, and Berlin, and at the Institute for Advanced Study. Born in Germany, Einstein became a Swiss citizen in 1901 and later an American citizen. He is best noted for his theory of relativity (restricted and general), the complete theory of Brownian motion, the theory of the photoelectric effect, and the quantum theory of radiant energy. Any of these investigations would be worthy of a Nobel Prize, and in 1921 he received this award for his discovery of the law of the "photoelectric effect."

$$\lambda = \frac{h}{mc} \qquad (4)$$

That is, a photon of mass m has associated with it a wavelength, λ.

The Detection of Electronic Waves

De Broglie's suggestions concerning "electronic waves" were verified when Davisson[8] and Germer[9] discovered that electrons could be diffracted in the same manner as electromagnetic waves. The introduction to their classic paper summarizes their work.

▼   "The investigation reported in this paper was begun as the result of an accident which occurred in this laboratory in April 1925. At that time we were continuing an investigation, first reported in 1921, of the distribution-in-angle of electrons scattered by a target of ordinary (polycrystalline) nickel. During the course of this work a liquid-air bottle exploded at a time when the target was at a high temperature; the experimental tube was broken, and the target heavily oxidized by the inrushing air. The oxide was eventually reduced and a layer of the target removed by vaporization, but only after prolonged heating at various high temperatures in hydrogen and in vacuum.

"When the experiments were continued it was found that the distribution-in-angle of the scattered electrons had been completely changed. Specimen curves exhibiting this alteration are shown in Figure 11–1. These curves are all for a bombarding potential of 75 volts. The electron beam is incident on the target from the right, and the intensities of scattering in different directions are proportional to the vectors from the point of bombardment to the curves. The upper curves (for different angles of incidence) are characteristic of the target prior to the accident. . . . The lower curves — obtained after the accident — were the first of their sort to be observed. This marked alteration in the scattering pattern was traced to a re-crystallization of the target that occurred during the prolonged heating. Before the accident and in previous experiments we had been bombarding many small crystals, but in the tests subsequent to the accident we were bombarding only a few large ones. The actual number was of the order of ten.

[8] Clinton Joseph Davisson (1881–1958): Member of the technical staff at Bell Laboratories (1917) and Professor of Physics at the University of Virginia (1946). Davisson's research interests were in the fields of thermionics, the scattering of electrons by solids, electron diffraction, and electron geometrical optics. In 1937 he shared the Nobel Prize in physics with G. P. Thomson.

[9] Lester Halbert Germer (1896–   ): Research physicist at Bell Telephone Laboratories. Germer's research interests are concerned with thermionics, electron diffraction, erosion of metals, contact physics, and surface physics.

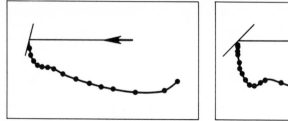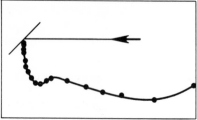

**SCATTERING OF 75 VOLT ELECTRONS FROM
A BLOCK OF NICKEL (MANY SMALL CRYSTALS)**

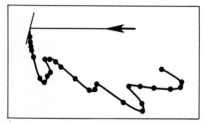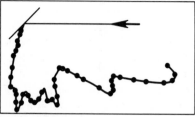

**SCATTERING OF 75 VOLT ELECTRONS FROM
SEVERAL LARGE NICKEL CRYSTALS**

FIGURE 11–1

*Scattering curves from nickel before and after crystal growth had
occurred.*

"It seemed probable from these results that the intensity of scattering
from a single crystal would exhibit a marked dependence on crystal direction, and we set about at once preparing experiments for an investigation
of this dependence. We must admit that the results obtained in these experiments have proved to be quite at variance with our expectations. It
seemed to us likely that strong beams would be found issuing from the
crystal along what may be termed its transparent directions — the directions in which the atoms in the lattice are arranged along the smallest
number of lines per unit area. Strong beams are indeed found issuing from
the crystal, but only when the speed of bombardment lies near one or
another of a series of critical values, and then in directions quite unrelated
to crystal transparency.

"The most striking characteristic of these beams is a one to one correspondence, presently to be described, which the strongest of them bear
to the Laue beams that would be found issuing from the same crystal if
the incident beam were a beam of X-rays. Certain others appear to be
analogues, not of Laue beams, but of optical diffraction beams from plane
reflection gratings — the lines of these gratings being lines or rows of

atoms in the surface of the crystal. Because of these similarities between the scattering of electrons by the crystal and the scattering of waves by three- and two-dimensional gratings a description of the occurrence and behavior of the electron diffraction beams in terms of the scattering of an equivalent wave radiation by the atoms of the crystal, and its subsequent interference, is not only possible, but most simple and natural. This involves the association of a wave-length with the incident electron beam, and this wave-length turns out to be in acceptable agreement with the value h/mv of the undulatory mechanics, Planck's action constant divided by the momentum of the electron."[10]   ▲

Theoretically, de Broglie's equation can be used to calculate the wave-length associated with any moving body. Thus an electron (with a mass of 9.1×10^{-28} g.) moving with a velocity of 5.9×10^8 cm./sec. has associated with it a wave motion of about 1.2 Å, whereas a baseball weighing 140 g. moving at 2.5×10^3 cm./sec. has a wavelength associated with it of 1.9×10^{-24} Å. It is apparent that objects we can see have a wave motion with a negligibly small wavelength compared to that of the visible light (4000 to 6000 Å) reflected from them into our eyes, whereas small objects such as electrons, which we could never hope to see, have wavelengths approaching those of X-rays. If X-rays are used in an attempt to detect the positions of electrons, the energies of the detecting radiation and of the electron are of the same magnitude, a situation that leads to a fundamental difficulty as we shall see later.

Up to this time electrons had been treated as hard spheres, the positions of which could be precisely determined. De Broglie suggested that a more fruitful approach to understanding the behavior of electrons lay in an investigation of their wave nature.

Electronic Waves and Atomic Structure

The problem of describing the motion of electrons about a nucleus now became one of portraying the wave motion associated with the moving electron. A given type of electronic motion will have a characteristic wave motion associated with it. For example, an electron moving in a circular orbit such as that shown in Figure 11–2 can have a variety of wave motions associated with it, the wavelengths being defined by Equation 4. Two possibilities exist for this simple periodic motion of the electron: either the wave associated with the moving electron will be reinforced as the electron completes successive orbits and a standing wave will be established (Figure 11–

[10] C. DAVISSON and L. H. GERMER, "Diffraction of Electrons by a Crystal of Nickel," *Physical Review,* **30,** 705 (1927).

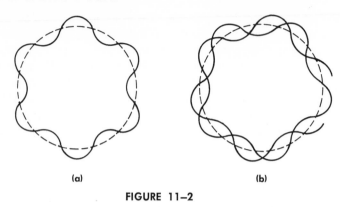

(a)   (b)

FIGURE 11–2

De Broglie waves for the circular orbits for a stationary state (a) and for a quantum mechanical excluded state where the waves are destroyed by interference.

2, a), or each successive orbit will generate waves which are out of phase and which will destroy one another by interference (Figure 11–2, b). Thus, a standing wave is obtained only in the case where the frequency (which is a measure of the energy of the electron; see Equation 1) is such that a *whole number* of waves just fit around the circle. Apparently, standing waves can exist only for certain frequencies for a given motion. If it is recalled that the frequency of a wave is a way of measuring the energy of an electron (Equation 1), the existence of standing waves for a given electron motion is the wave-equivalent manner of stating that electrons moving about nuclei can have only discrete energies. If the electron has any other frequency (energy), the waves destroy each other. De Broglie thus arrived at the Bohr *postulate* — that electrons can occupy only certain orbits with discrete energies — from a direct consideration of the waves associated with the electrons.

The description of electronic motion in terms of the waves associated with the electron leads to an important conclusion. In classical mechanics, it is normally assumed that the properties of a system can be described to as high a degree of precision as necessary. Knowing the position and velocity, for example, of a billiard ball moving across a table at a given instant, from classical mechanics we could predict the position of the ball at any future time. However, in the study of systems involving very small particles, an uncertainty is unavoidably introduced into the quantities measured by the process of measurement itself. This situation arises because very small moving particles, like electrons, have energies comparable to the energies of the photons with which they can be observed. In other words, "observation" of the position of an electron involves the reflection of a photon into the measuring instrument. Since the photon has energy of the same order of magnitude as the electron, the act of observation itself causes the electron to be displaced.

After the photon is reflected into the measuring instrument and detected, we know where the electron was at the moment of reflection but not where it was at the moment the photon was detected. Heisenberg[11] showed that there is a fundamental limit to the precision with which both the position *and* the velocity of a particle can be known that is independent of the refinement of our measuring instruments. It follows from Heisenberg's uncertainty principle that if we know the exact position of the particle in question, we do not know its precise velocity, and if we know its precise velocity, we do not know exactly where it is.

In the theory of electromagnetic wave propagation, the wavelength, frequency, and velocity of the wave are related by Equation 5. For electromag-

$$\lambda \nu = c \qquad (5)$$

netic radiation, c is constant so that the wavelength and frequency are not independent variables. However, the *intensity* of the electromagnetic radiation is given by the amplitude, or relative height, of the wave. Thus, the brightness of two beams of monochromatic radiation could be discussed in terms of the relative amplitudes of the waves which constitute the beams; an analogous discussion of these beams in terms of the photon theory of electromagnetic radiation would involve the relative number of photons in the two beams, the more intense beam having the greater number of photons. The number of moving particles and the amplitude of the waves associated with the particles are directly related.

The concept of waves associated with electrons and its consequences meant that a description of the atom different from that developed by Bohr was possible. In the new description the exact positions of the electrons involved were of less importance than in the Bohr theory. Instead, an atom such as hydrogen was considered simply to have a nucleus with an electron moving about it; the emphasis was placed on describing the nature of the waves associated with this electronic motion. It was not necessary to consider all of the possible wave motions of the electron, since the only motions that had a physical meaning were those in which the waves associated with the electron reinforced each other and established a standing wave. As indicated previously, the waves associated with most of the periodic motions of the electron destroyed each other. Since the amplitude of a wave is proportional to the number of particles associated with the wave, where the periodic motion of the electron gives a summation of waves which corresponds to a wave with

[11] Werner Heisenberg (1901–   ): Director of the Kaiser Wilhelm Institute of Physics (later known as the Max Planck Institute). Heisenberg's outstanding contributions have been in matrix mechanics, and his enunciation of the uncertainty principle has had a profound influence on the course of physics. In 1932 he received the Nobel Prize in physics "for the creation of quantum mechanics, the application of which has led to the discovery of the allotropic forms of hydrogen."

zero (or low) amplitude (Figure 11–2), there are no (or very few) particles moving with that energy. On the other hand, the periodic motion for which the waves reinforce each other and a standing wave results (Figure 11–2) corresponds to particles moving with a discrete energy. Thus, the establishment of standing waves is equivalent to Bohr's condition that electrons have only discrete energies.

THE SCHRÖDINGER EQUATION

We have discussed the wave-mechanical description of electronic motion in two dimensions. It is apparent, although more difficult to visualize, that a similar situation exists for electrons moving in three dimensions about a nucleus. The problem becomes a matter of determining the motions of electrons for which standing waves are established, a question that was posed and solved by Erwin Schrödinger[12] in 1926.

Let us assume that at any instant we can observe an electron in its motion about a nucleus. The electron, at that instant, will be located at a point, $x, y, z,$ with respect to the nucleus, and will possess a total energy (E) comprised of potential energy (V), with respect to the nucleus, plus kinetic energy. At that point in space the three-dimensional wave will have a certain amplitude, ψ. Schrödinger showed that these quantities are related by the so-called wave equation (Equation 6),

$$\frac{\partial^2 \psi}{\partial x^2} + \frac{\partial^2 \psi}{\partial y^2} + \frac{\partial^2 \psi}{\partial z^2} + \frac{8\pi^2 m}{h^2}(E - V)\psi = 0 \qquad (6)$$

where m represents the mass of an electron, E the total energy of the system, and V the potential energy.

To determine the distribution of electrons about the atom, it is necessary to solve the wave equation for ψ at each point for all possible electronic motions and then to sum up all the values of ψ. In this manner, we could calculate the amplitude of the electronic wave at each point, which would be a measure of the electronic density at those points. Schrödinger's equation is a differential one, the symbol $\dfrac{\partial^2}{\partial x^2}$ representing, for example, the summation of the amplitude in the x-direction. For our purposes, it is not necessary to go into the details of solving the wave equation; suffice it to say that the value of ψ at each point about the nucleus can be obtained. The only restriction

[12] Erwin Schrödinger (1887–1961): Professor of Physics at Stuttgart, Breslau, Zürich, Oxford, Graz, and Berlin, and Director of the Dublin Institute for Advanced Studies (1940). Schrödinger's major effort was in the field of wave mechanics as applied to the structure of matter. In 1933 he won the Nobel Prize in physics (shared with Dirac).

necessary for the solution of the wave equation is that ψ represent a solution that corresponds to standing waves rather than one for which the waves destroy each other.

The Quantum Numbers

It is a characteristic of differential equations that they can have several solutions, the difference between the solutions being a constant factor. The solutions of the Schrödinger equation as written for three dimensions are characterized by three integers — the quantum numbers. These are designated n, l, and m and are called the principal quantum number, the azimuthal quantum number, and the magnetic quantum number, respectively. The quantum numbers are related to each other and can take on only certain values. The principal quantum number, n, can have any integral value except zero ($n = 1, 2, 3, 4, \ldots$). The azimuthal quantum number, l, can have any integral value including zero ($l = 0, 1, 2, 3, \ldots n - 1$), and for any value of the azimuthal quantum number m (the magnetic quantum number) can have the values $\pm l$, $\pm(l - 1)$, $\pm(l - 2)$, $\ldots .0$. The relationships among the quantum numbers are shown in Table 11–1.

TABLE 11–1

Relationships Among the Principal Quantum (n), Azimuthal Quantum (l), and Magnetic Quantum (m) Numbers

n	l	m
1	0 (s)	0
2	0 (s)	0
	1 (p)	$-1, 0, +1$
3	0 (s)	0
	1 (p)	$-1, 0, +1$
	2 (d)	$-2, -1, 0, +1, +2$
4	0 (s)	0
	1 (p)	$-1, 0, +1$
	2 (d)	$-2, -1, 0, +1, +2$
	3 (f)	$-3, -2, -1, 0, +1, +2, +3$

The quantum numbers are used to designate the solutions of the wave equation, i.e., solutions to Equation 6, which correspond to the motions of electrons for which standing waves are established. Since the solutions of the wave equation represent, in a sense, the allowed motions of the electron about the nucleus, or areas about the nucleus where the electron density is high, the solutions are called orbits or orbitals. Historically, these orbits have been designated by the quantum numbers which represent that solution. In addition, the quantum number l is usually given a letter designation rather than a numerical value, $l = 0$, 1, 2, 3 being designated s, p, d, and f, respectively. Thus, the orbital (solution to the wave equation) which is defined by $n = 1$ and $l = 0$ is designated a $1s$ orbital, and a $4p$ orbital is the solution of the wave equation represented by the quantum numbers $n = 4$ and $l = 1$.

The solutions of the wave equation not only represent the allowed energy states of an electron, but they also permit the calculation of the amplitude of the wave associated with an electron at any point about the nucleus. Since the amplitude of the electronic wave is related to the electronic density, it is possible to determine where the electronic density is greatest for each of the orbits. Figure 11–3 shows the distribution of electronic density about the nucleus of an atom. Calculations show that the most important considerations in determining the shapes of atomic orbitals are the values of the azimuthal quantum number, l, and the magnetic quantum number, m. A variation of the principal quantum number merely changes the relative size of the orbital. Thus, all s orbitals (i.e., solutions for the wave equation for which $l = 0$) are spherically symmetrical (Figure 11–3, a). Orbitals for which $l = 1$, i.e., p orbitals, are dumbbell-shaped (Figure 11–3, b). It should be recalled that, for the quantum number $l = 1$, there are three possible values for the magnetic quantum number, i.e., $m = -1, 0, +1$. Since the magnetic quantum number reflects the orientation of the orbitals in space, five different spatial orientations are possible for d orbitals ($l = 2$), as shown in Figure 11–3, c. It must be emphasized that the orbitals pictured in Figure 11–3 represent the areas in space about an atom where the electronic density is high, or, in other words, where the probability of finding an electron is high.

The relative energies of the various orbits are given in Figure 11–4. For the sake of clarity, all the orbits with the same azimuthal quantum number have been placed in one column; no significance should be attached to the horizontal displacement of the energy levels. It should be noted that the $1s$ energy level is lower than a $2s$ energy level which is lower than a $2p$ level, etc.[13]

The wave-mechanical picture of an atom gives us the distribution of electrons in space as well as the relative energies of the orbitals. The latter provides the basis for the periodic classification of the elements while the former holds the key to the structure of molecules.

Electron Spin

Before considering the wave-mechanical explanation of the periodic arrangement of the elements, two subjects should be discussed, the concept of

---

[13] Another way of stating this is to say that a $1s$ orbital is of lower energy than a $2s$ orbital which is of lower energy than a $2p$ orbital, etc.

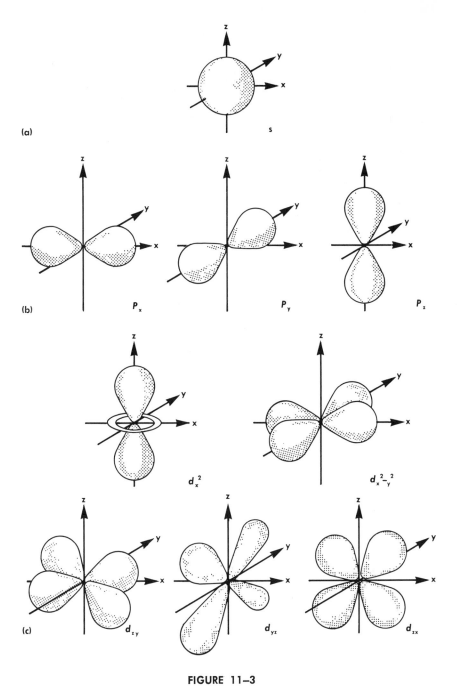

FIGURE 11–3

The distribution of electronic density in s, p, and d orbitals.

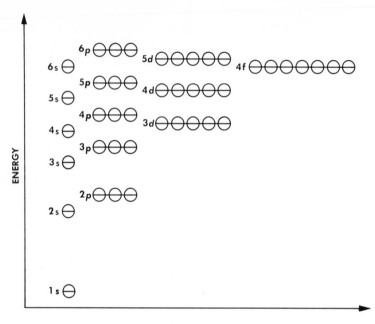

FIGURE 11–4

The relative order of atomic energy levels.

electron spin and the Pauli[14] exclusion principle. Since the Schrödinger equation yields only three quantum numbers, the electron spin must be introduced as a separate concept, as suggested by Lewis in explaining the magnetism of certain species.

Originally, the concept of electron spin was introduced to eliminate the discrepancies which arose in the Bohr theory when it was applied to explain the details of the fine structure of the hydrogen spectrum. Two Dutch scientists, Uhlenbeck[15] and Goudsmit,[16] resolved the inability of Bohr's original

[14] Wolfgang Ernst Pauli (1900–1958): Professor of Theoretical Physics at Zürich (1928), at the Institute for Advanced Study (1940), and again at Zürich (1946). A student of Sommerfeld, Pauli contributed to the relativity theory, the theory of paramagnetism of metals, the quantum mechanical description of electrons in metals, and the discovery of the neutrino. In 1945, Pauli won the Nobel Prize in physics.

[15] George Eugen Uhlenbeck (1900–   ): Professor of Physics at Utrecht (1935), at the University of Michigan (1939), and at The Rockefeller Institute (1960). Uhlenbeck's research interests are in the theory of atomic structure, quantum mechanics, statistical mechanics and the kinetic theory of matter, and nuclear physics.

[16] Samuel Abraham Goudsmit (1902–   ): Professor of Physics at the University of Michigan (1932), Northwestern University (1946), and presently chairman of the physics department at Brookhaven National Laboratory. Goudsmit's work has been concerned with the theory of spectra and atomic structure, nuclear spin, and statistical problems in physics.

three quantum numbers to describe completely the motions of the electron by introducing the idea that an electron can spin on its axis.

▼ "In fact it seems that the introduction of the concept of the spinning electron makes it possible throughout to maintain the principle of the successive building up of atoms utilized by Bohr in his discussion of the relations between spectra and the natural system of the elements."[17] ▲

Not only did their suggestion alleviate the difficulties in interpreting the fine structure of the hydrogen atom, but it also made clear the relationship of extranuclear electron structure to the periodic arrangement of the elements. To the three quantum numbers which have been given physical significance must be added the spin quantum number, s.[18] Since an electron can spin in only one of two directions, i.e., clockwise or counterclockwise, the spin quantum number can have a value of $+\frac{1}{2}$ or $-\frac{1}{2}$.

Although the concept of electronic spin has been introduced here apart from the wave-mechanical concepts of Schrödinger, a more detailed analysis of the quantum theory by P. A. M. Dirac,[19] which incorporates the relativity theory, yields the spin quantum number without an *a priori* postulate.

THE ELECTRONIC STRUCTURE OF THE ATOM

Although we are now in a position to consider the distribution of electrons among the various orbitals of an atom, we need to follow only *two* guiding principles. First, an electron will seek the lowest energy orbital available (this is a restatement of the familiar fundamental law of physics which states that a system will achieve the lowest energy state possible). The second principle was first explicitly stated by Wolfgang Pauli and is now referred to as the Pauli exclusion principle, i.e., "that in any system, whether a single atom or a molecule, no two electrons could be assigned the same set of four quantum numbers."[20] By knowing the relationship between the quantum numbers (Table 11-1) and using the Pauli exclusion principle, it is possible to determine the total number of electrons in each orbital (Table 11-2). Thus, in the first orbital ($n = 1$), there can be only two electrons, one with

[17] G. E. UHLENBECK and S. GOUDSMIT, "Spinning Electrons and the Structure of Spectra," *Nature,* **117**, 265 (1926).

[18] Not to be confused with the designation of s for orbitals in which $l = 0$.

[19] Paul Adrian Maurice Dirac (1902–   ): Professor of Mathematics at Cambridge University. Dirac is best known for his elucidation of the mathematical intricacies of quantum mechanics. In 1933 he shared the Nobel Prize in physics (with E. Schrödinger) "for the discovery of new fertile forms of the atomic theory."

[20] W. Pauli, "Concerning the Connection of the Agreement between Electron Groups in the Atom and the Fine Structure of Their Spectra," *Zeitschrift für Physik,* **31**, 776 (1925).

the quantum numbers $n = 1$, $l = 0$, $m = 0$, $s = +\frac{1}{2}$ and one with the quantum numbers $n = 1$, $l = 0$, $m = 0$, $s = -\frac{1}{2}$. It is impossible for the first orbital to contain a third electron because it would have to be assigned the same set of quantum numbers used to designate one of the first two electrons, an occurrence which the Pauli exclusion principle prohibits. An inspection of Table 11–2 shows that the maximum number of electrons in each con-

TABLE 11–2

Determination of the Total Number of Electrons in Each Orbital

n	l	m	s	Total number of electrons
1	$0\,(s)$	0	$\pm\frac{1}{2}$	2
2	$0\,(s)$	0	$\pm\frac{1}{2}$	2 ⎫
	$1\,(p)$	−1	$\pm\frac{1}{2}$	2 ⎫ ⎬ 8
		0	$\pm\frac{1}{2}$	2 ⎬ 6
		+1	$\pm\frac{1}{2}$	2 ⎭
3	$0\,(s)$	0	$\pm\frac{1}{2}$	2 ⎫
	$1\,(p)$	−1	$\pm\frac{1}{2}$	2 ⎫
		0	$\pm\frac{1}{2}$	2 ⎬ 6
		+1	$\pm\frac{1}{2}$	2 ⎭ ⎬ 18
	$2\,(d)$	−2	$\pm\frac{1}{2}$	2 ⎫
		−1	$\pm\frac{1}{2}$	2
		0	$\pm\frac{1}{2}$	2 ⎬ 10
		+1	$\pm\frac{1}{2}$	2
		+2	$\pm\frac{1}{2}$	2 ⎭

secutive principal orbital, $n = 1$, 2, and 3, is two, eight, and eighteen, respectively. In addition, orbitals with the same azimuthal quantum number (l) contain the same maximum number of electrons; e.g., a maximum of two electrons is designated s ($l = 0$), six electrons are designated p ($l = 1$), and ten electrons are designated d ($l = 2$).

ELECTRONIC DISTRIBUTION AND PERIODICITY

The elements in the periodic chart can be built up, beginning with hydrogen, in the following manner. Consider that the relative energies of the orbitals are given by Figure 11–4 and that the distribution of electrons in an atom can be derived by adding one electron to an atom with an atomic number one unit smaller. Thus we need only to consider the allocation of one electron at a time. Hydrogen has one electron in the lowest orbital available, i.e., the orbital for which $n = 1$, $l = 0$ ($1s$), as shown in Table 11–3. Helium has an atomic number of 2 and, hence, has one electron more than hydrogen. According to the scheme proposed, one electron is added to the hydrogen structure to obtain the distribution of electrons in helium; the second electron can be assigned to the same orbital as the first electron if its spin is opposite to that of the first electron. Thus, helium would have two electrons of opposite spins in the 1*s* orbital (Table 11–3). Addition of an electron to the structure of the helium atom yields the distribution of electrons expected for the next element, lithium. The third electron cannot be placed in the 1*s* orbital without a violation of the Pauli exclusion principle and therefore must be placed in the next lowest available orbital (Table 11–2) which is designated 2*s* (Table 11–3). Addition of a fourth electron fills the 2*s* orbital,

TABLE 11–3

Electronic Configuration of the First Eighteen Elements in the Periodic Classification

Element	Atomic number	Orbital					
		1*s*	2*s*	2*p*	3*s*	3*p*	3*d*
H	1	1					
He	2	2					
Li	3	2	1				
Be	4	2	2				
B	5	2	2	1			
C	6	2	2	2			
N	7	2	2	3			
O	8	2	2	4			
F	9	2	2	5			
Ne	10	2	2	6			
Na	11	2	2	6	1		
Mg	12	2	2	6	2		
Al	13	2	2	6	2	1	
Si	14	2	2	6	2	2	
P	15	2	2	6	2	3	
S	16	2	2	6	2	4	
Cl	17	2	2	6	2	5	
A	18	2	2	6	2	6	

so the fifth electron must be placed in a new orbital, the 2*p* orbital. A glance at Table 11–2 shows that orbitals designated *p* (*l* = 1) can contain a maximum of six electrons, three with spins in one direction and three with opposite spins. The successive addition of these six electrons corresponds to the formation of the elements boron, carbon, nitrogen, oxygen, fluorine, and neon. After the 2*p* orbital is filled, the next one available is the 3*s* orbital, which can contain two electrons; the filling of this orbital corresponds to the formation of sodium and magnesium. The next available orbital is a 3*p* orbital, which, like the 2*p* orbital, can hold six electrons. The filling of this orbital corresponds to the formation of aluminum, silicon, phosphorus, sulfur, chlorine, and argon. Thus, the electronic structure of all of the elements can be determined by the successive addition of electrons to the orbitals available.

The distribution of electrons for the first eighteen elements, as illustrated in Table 11–3, shows a periodic behavior. The alkali metals, Li and Na (as well as K, Rb, Cs, and Fr, for which the electronic distributions are not given) have one electron in the outer shell. Be and Mg have two electrons, B and Al three, C and Si four, N and P five, S and O six, F and Cl seven, and Ne and A eight. A detailed study of the periodic chart, with respect to the electronic configuration of the elements according to the principles outlined above, shows that families of elements are characterized by the type of valence orbital their electrons occupy (Figure 11–5). The elements of groups IA and IIA have one and two electrons, respectively, in s orbitals. The elements of groups IIIA, IVA, VA, VIA, VIIA, and VIII contain one, two, three, four, five, and six electrons, respectively, in p orbitals; the transition elements have d orbitals that are being filled and the rare earths have f orbitals that are being filled.

From a casual consideration, it might not appear that the motion of electrons about a nucleus could be successfully described by the wave-mechanical approach because of the nebulous manner in which the electron is described. However, a detailed study of this model brought scientists to a more complete understanding of the basis of the periodic classification of the elements than did any of the earlier considerations; it should be noted, however, that all the previous relationships, for example, the Lewis octet theory, are still valid. More important, the model of the atom is a dynamic one in the sense that the electrons are in rapid motion and the distribution of electrons in orbitals is considered as a whole rather than as a detailed account of the pathway an electron traverses in its journey about an atom. Such considerations had been suggested by Lewis in his arguments against the Bohr atomic model (page 103). Only a few years after Lewis had presented his objections, J. H. VAN VLECK[21] touched on the same points in a discussion of the wave-mechanical atomic model.

▼   "The chemist has often thought that he has found strong evidence on the instantaneous positions of electrons, and first and last there has been considerable controversy as to whether the facts of organic chemistry can be explained as well by assuming that the electrons are moving, as the physicist would like, as by supposing that they are standing still. However, is it really necessary to suppose that the structural bonds of the organic chemists represent instantaneous positions of the electrons, or would it not do just as well to suppose that they represent average positions, for the mathematics indicates that it is the average rather than instantaneous positions of the electrons which determine whether the nuclei are in equilibrium?

[21] John Hasbrouck Van Vleck (1899–   ): Professor at the University of Minnesota (1927), Wisconsin (1928), and at Harvard (1934). Van Vleck's research is concerned with the quantum theory of atomic structure and magnetism.

FIGURE 11–5

The periodic classification of the elements.

IA	IIA													IIIA	IVA	VA	VIA	VIIA	VIII
1 H																			2 He
3 Li	4 Be													5 B	6 C	7 N	8 O	9 F	10 Ne
11 Na	12 Mg													13 Al	14 Si	15 P	16 S	17 Cl	18 A
19 K	20 Ca	21 Sc	22 Ti	23 V	24 Cr	25 Mn	26 Fe	27 Co	28 Ni	29 Cu	30 Zn			31 Ga	32 Ge	33 As	34 Se	35 Br	36 Kr
37 Rb	38 Sr	39 Y	40 Zr	41 Nb	42 Mo	43 Tc	44 Ru	45 Rh	46 Pd	47 Ag	48 Cd			49 In	50 Sn	51 Sb	52 Te	53 I	54 Xe
55 Cs	56 Ba	71 Lu	72 Hf	73 Ta	74 W	75 Re	76 Os	77 Ir	78 Pt	79 Au	80 Hg			81 Tl	82 Pb	83 Bi	84 Po	85 At	86 Rn
87 Fr	88 Ra																		

57 La	58 Ce	59 Pr	60 Nd	61 Pm	62 Sm	63 Eu	64 Gd	65 Tb	66 Dy	67 Ho	68 Er	69 Tm	70 Yb
89 Ac	90 Th	91 Pa	92 U	93 Np	94 Pu	95 Am	96 Cm	97 Bk	98 Cf				

s   d   f   p

"There is, of course, much evidence for tetrahedral models of the carbon atom, but does this necessarily mean that the instantaneous positions of the electrons project out in four directions; could not this evidence mean that this symmetry is only true of average positions of the electrons, or even that there is some dynamical function, important for the mechanics of chemical combination, but without any immediate geometrical significance, which is symmetrical mathematically in the variables representing the co-ordinates of the four electrons?

"According to the theoretical physicist, one has no right to speak of the *instantaneous* position of the electron in its path within the atom, for if one knew where the electron were located each successive instant of time, one would know both the position and velocity of the electron, which we have seen is contrary to the Heisenberg indeterminism principle. It can, however, be shown that it is legitimate to introduce the concept of the *average* position of the electron."[22]   ▲

We have arrived at the point where the modern concept of a chemical bond can be considered. Lewis correlated the electronic structure of atoms with their chemical characteristics and suggested that a covalent bond between atoms consists of a shared pair of electrons. Quantum mechanics provided a more detailed picture of electron distribution within an atom than did the Bohr theory. The techniques of quantum mechanics were also applied successfully to the problem of electron distribution within molecules.

SUGGESTED READING

Bernal, J. D. "Structure of Liquids," *Scientific American,* **203,** No. 2, 125 (1960).
Darrow, K. K. "The Quantum Theory," *Scientific American,* **186,** No. 3, 47 (1952).
Luder, W. F. "Electron Configuration as the Basis of the Periodic Table," *Journal of Chemical Education,* **20,** 21 (1943).
Mendelssohn, K. "Probability Enters Physics," *American Scientist,* **49,** 37 (1961).
Noller, C. R. "A Physical Picture of Covalent Bonding and Resonance in Organic Chemistry," *Journal of Chemical Education,* **27,** 504 (1950).
Schrödinger, E. "What Is Matter?" *Scientific American,* **180,** No. 3, 52 (1953).

[22] J. H. VAN VLECK, "The New Quantum Mechanics," *Chemical Reviews,* **5,** 477 (1928).

CHAPTER 12

The Chemical Bond

The successful use of wave mechanics in describing atomic structure naturally led to the suggestion that a similar approach could be used to describe the electronic distribution in a chemical bond. In the case of an atomic species, the electrons move under the influence of a single positive nucleus, but, in a simple molecule such as hydrogen, the electrons move under the influence of two nuclei. With more complex combinations of atoms, the electrons could conceivably be influenced by all nuclei present. These ideas were summarized by VAN VLECK in the following words:

▼   "The mathematical problem of a chemical reaction seems to be this: to investigate whether there are stable solutions of the Schroedinger wave equation corresponding to the interaction between two (or more) atoms, using only the wave functions which have the type of symmetry compatible with Pauli's exclusion principle."[1]   ▲

THE WAVE-MECHANICAL CONCEPT OF THE CHEMICAL BOND

The problem of describing the electronic distribution in the simplest of all stable molecules, H_2, was first attacked on a wave-mechanical basis by Heitler and London. In their analysis, H_2 was considered as a system comprised of two hydrogen nuclei, A and B, and two electrons, 1 and 2 (Figure 12–1). The electrical forces operative in this system were the repulsion of the two nuclei, the repulsion of the two electrons, the attraction of nucleus A for each

[1] J. H. VAN VLECK, "The New Quantum Mechanics," *Chemical Reviews,* **5,** 500 (1928).

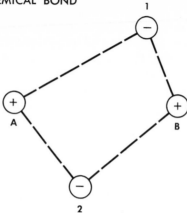

FIGURE 12–1

In the H_2 molecule, the two hydrogen nuclei, A and B, repel each other; the two electrons, 1 and 2, repel each other; and each hydrogen nucleus attracts both electrons.

electron, and the attraction of nucleus B for each electron. The Schrödinger equation can be applied to this system and ψ, the solution to the equation, is proportional to the electronic density at a given point in space. As in the case of atomic systems, the object is to solve the equation for ψ. Unfortunately, the solution of the Schrödinger equation for even the simplest molecule, H_2, is much more difficult than that for atomic systems and thus solutions must be obtained by approximation methods. Many physicists, chemists, and mathematicians have contributed to the methods which are now used to solve the wave equations written for molecular systems, and, rather than discuss these developments, which would be an exercise in mathematics, it better suits our purposes to present the results of their manipulations.

Scientists quickly realized the difficulty in obtaining exact solutions to the Schrödinger wave equation applied to systems involving more than one atomic nucleus; the method introduced by Heitler and London in 1927 was, historically, the first method of approximation. Since the object of solving the Schrödinger wave equation is to obtain the value of the wave function, ψ, at each point in space, and since an exact solution is impossible for even the simplest cases, the only alternative which remains is to guess at the mathematical nature of the solution.

Perhaps a simple analogy would be useful here to clarify our case. Suppose that we lived in a world where simple algebraic manipulations were unknown to us. Many everyday problems could still be solved by approximation methods. For example, the simple problem, "How many apples costing 6 cents each can be purchased for 84 cents?" might be solved by the following thought process. One apple costs 6 cents, two apples cost 12 cents, three apples cost 18 cents. At this point, it is obvious that 18 cents is a lot less than 84 cents; perhaps, then, we could find the answer by guessing that the correct number of apples is 10. We soon discover, however, that 10 apples cost 60 cents, and again it is obvious that the price of 10 apples will not consume the 84 cents we have to spend. At least, though, we did not need to go through the cost of 4, 5, 6, 7, 8, and 9 apples, even though we have not solved our problem. We might guess now that 20 apples is the correct answer. But, since 20 apples cost $1.20, we find that in this case we have guessed too high. Now we know that the number of apples we can purchase is somewhere between 10 and 20. Intuition might suggest that the next guess be 15. At 6 cents apiece, then, 15 apples cost 90 cents, and we now see that we are only 6 cents in excess of the total amount of money we have to spend, meaning that 1 apple less than 15, or 14 apples, should be the correct number of apples we can purchase for 84 cents. There is, of course, a much easier way to obtain an answer to the original problem, but the process just described serves to illustrate the basis of approximation methods: once the relationship between several factors is known (1 apple costs 6 cents), the answer to the problem can be obtained by guessing at possible solutions.

Valence-Bond Approximation

The Heitler-London method, which employed essentially the foregoing process for obtaining the solution of the wave equation, has been modified several times and is now called the valence-bond method. It should be recalled that the wave functions, ψ, for atomic systems represent solutions of the Schrödinger equation for standing waves which describe the electronic density about the nucleus. As two atoms are brought together to form a bond, it might be expected that the standing waves associated with each atom would interact to form a new standing wave for the whole molecule. If the wave function for the whole molecule could be mathematically described, it would represent the solution of the Schrödinger equation. An approximate solution to the wave equation can be obtained by combining the atomic wave equations. Thus, the hydrogen molecule might be thought of as being formed from two hydrogen atoms, A and B, each with its own electron. A reasonable approximation of the wave function for the molecule is obtained when the atomic wave functions are combined. This corresponds to assuming that, in the structure of the hydrogen molecule, the electrons are completely under the influence of their respective nuclei, i.e., in the structure $H_A e_1 + H_B e_2$ (for which the molecular wave function can be designated ψ_1), neither electron feels the presence of the other nucleus. However, an equivalent structure may be assumed which depicts the electron originally associated with a given nucleus as having traded places with the other electron; this structure can be designated as $H_A e_2 + H_B e_1$, ψ_2 representing this molecular wave function.

Obviously, these two possibilities are indistinguishable since they differ only in the labeling of the electrons. We know immediately that neither structure can be correct because the electrons involved in bond formation are always influenced by *both* nuclei. We might suspect that the wave function, ψ, for the molecule, H_2, would be a combination of the wave function, ψ_1, for the structure, $H_A e_1 + H_B e_2$, and ψ_2, for the structure $H_A e_2 + H_B e_1$. However, this combination can be made in two ways: $\psi_+ = C_1\psi_1 + C_2\psi_2$ or $\psi_- = C_1\psi_1 - C_2\psi_2$.[2] It can be shown that (1) ψ_+ represents the electronic distribution which corresponds to the formation of a stable system, that is, where sufficient electron density exists in the region between the nuclei to allow the formation of a bond; and that (2) ψ_- corresponds to the situation where there is relatively little electron density between the nuclei, indicating repulsion of the two hydrogen atoms. VAN VLECK describes this process succinctly.

▼ "Chemists have often asked me this question, 'Where are the electrons located in, say, the bond between two hydrogen atoms to form a hydrogen molecule. Does each electron remain with its own nucleus, or are the two electrons shared 50–50 by both nuclei.' According to the quantum mechanics, the latter alternative comes the closer to the true state of affairs, for in the hydrogen molecule the average electronic charge distribution is symmetrical with respect to the two nuclei, and the two electrons are continually exchanging places, so that it is impossible to say which electron belongs with which nucleus. When the hydrogen atoms are too far apart to form a molecule, say at a distance 3×10^{-7} cm. comparable with the distances of approach between molecules in the kinetic theory of gases, the exchange of places is very infrequent, only about once in 10^{30} years on the average, whereas when the atoms are so closely knit together as to form a molecule, the exchange transpires on the average about 10^{10} times per second! The statistical or average charge distribution in the hydrogen molecule can be calculated directly from the quantum postulates, and is shown in Figure 12–2, taken from a paper by London. The contour lines in these figures represent the statistical charge density. Thus this density is large where the lines are close together, and small where they are far apart. The densest region is, of course, in general near the two nuclei. The mathematical analysis shows that there are two solutions of the Schroedinger wave equation corresponding to the interaction between two hydrogen atoms. In one of them, shown in Figure 12–3, the forces exerted on the nuclei are entirely of a repulsive nature. The meaning of this is that two hydrogen atoms may be brought into contact without necessarily forming a molecule. In the other solution, Figure 12–2, there is attraction as

[2] C_1 and C_2 are constants chosen so that ψ represents a minimum in energy.

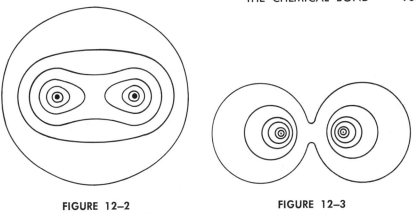

FIGURE 12-2   **FIGURE 12-3**

Attraction.   *Repulsion.*

well as repulsion, and this is what makes possible the formation of a stable molecule. It is seen from Figure 12–2 that in this other solution the negative electronic charge tends to pile up between the two nuclei, and it is the attraction of this negative charge which tends to bring the nuclei together and offsets the purely repulsive forces which exist between two positive charges by themselves. In the solution shown in Figure 12–2, the nuclei are in positions of equilibrium, whereas in Figure 12–3 they will fly apart.

"The concept of a statistical or average charge density, such as is shown in Figures 12–2 and 12–3, can perhaps be rendered more graphic by the following comparison. Supposing one were to photograph a swarm of fireflies at night by means of an exceedingly sensitive camera. If one were to take an instantaneous photograph or "snap-shot," each firefly would appear as a bright point on the photographic plate. If we took snap-shots at frequent intervals we could then trace the motion of each of the flies. Suppose, however, that instead we were to take a time exposure extending over a long period. Then the luminous points would be blurred out into a cloud of light upon the plate. The cloud would be brightest where the fireflies are most apt to congregate. Now the information which it is possible to obtain about the motion of the electron within the atom in quantum mechanics is analogous to that given by the time exposure in the firefly illustration. The statistical charge density corresponds to the density of the luminous cloud. Efforts have sometimes been made to interpret the electron in quantum mechanics as itself a sort of nebulous body spread over the entire atom, but that is no more correct than to say that a firefly is a bright cloud extending over a large distance. In either case it is only the time average of position that has the cloud or fluid-like appearance."[3] ▲

[3] *Ibid.,* p. 478.

In spite of the fact that the combination of wave functions designated by ψ_+ yields a picture of the hydrogen molecule whose greatest electron density lies between the nuclei, we need assurance that the properties of the molecule as calculated by our model correspond with those experimentally obtained. If they do not correspond we know that the model must be altered. The bond energy, or the amount of energy required to separate the atoms involved in the bond, is one characteristic property which can be calculated by knowing the solution to the Schrödinger equation. We have seen that ψ_+ corresponds to a possible solution of the Schrödinger equation for the hydrogen molecule. The suitability of the solution can now be determined by calculating the bond energy and comparing it with the measured bond energy. As a result, we learn that the calculated energy is 72.3 kcal./mole, whereas the experimental value is 108.8 kcal./mole. Apparently, then, ψ_+ is not a very good approximation for the solution to the Schrödinger equation as applied to the hydrogen molecule! The discrepancy in our findings can be attributed to the rather arbitrary process by which we decided on the functions used in calculating ψ_+. In fact, the only advantage to using these functions was that the atomic wave functions were already known.

A better wave function for the solution to the Schrödinger equation for H_2 involves the additional structures, $H_A{}^+ + (H_B e_2 e_1)^-$, described by ψ_3, and $(H_A e_1 e_2)^- + H_B{}^+$, described by ψ_4. In these structures, both electrons are associated with only one hydrogen atom, thereby giving it a unit negative charge, while the other hydrogen atom lacks an electron, thereby carrying a unit positive charge. Two such structures can be written since it is possible to have both electrons on either atom A or B. The wave functions ψ_3 and ψ_4 can also be constructed from atomic-like functions since one of the atoms involved in each of these structures has no electrons, and the other atom has a helium-like structure. Whereas in the previous instance only two structures were considered, for this approximation to the answer of the Schrödinger equation we are summing up the wave functions for all four structures.

$$\psi_+{}' = C_1\psi_1 + C_2\psi_2 + C_3\psi_3 + C_4\psi_4 \tag{1}$$

By using $\psi_+{}'$ as an approximate solution to the Schrödinger wave equation for the H_2 molecule, the energy of the system is calculated as 92.2 kcal./mole as compared with the experimental energy of 108.8 kcal./mole. Thus, our new approximation, $\psi_+{}'$, is considerably better than the first approximation, ψ_+.

It should be emphasized at this point that more refined calculations which take into account the repulsions between like-charged particles in this system eventually lead to a very good estimate of ψ_+. In arriving at the approximation to the solution of the Schrödinger wave equation for this simple system, we have started with atomic wave functions only because these functions have been worked out previously. The functions were chosen by writing down the possible Lewis electron-dot structures for the system. None of these structures, taken individually, was sufficient to yield a proper solution and hence did not represent the correct structure; the fact that the summation of the wave functions for each structure did yield a good solution can be interpreted to mean that the true structure of the hydrogen molecule is the summation of all of these individual structures (called resonance or canonical structures). Thus, in attempting to describe the electronic structure of so simple a system as the hydrogen molecule, we have seen that the best wave function is one composed of various proportions of the structures shown in Figure 12–4. It should be emphasized that the resonance structures shown

$$H^{e_1} \quad _{e_2}H \qquad\qquad H^{e_2} \quad _{e_1}H$$

$$H^{e_1-}_{e_2} \quad H^+ \qquad\qquad H^+ \quad ^{e_1}_{e_2}H^-$$

FIGURE 12–4

The valence-bond structures for the hydrogen molecule.

in Figure 12–4 are *not* different forms of the hydrogen molecule; taken together, the wave functions for the resonance structures yield a single wave function which accurately describes the real hydrogen molecule.[4]

It might appear that the valence-bond method of describing molecules more complex than hydrogen would become unwieldy with respect to the number of resonance structures which could be written; however, a judicious choice of the structures that are probably most important can often be made on the basis of chemical intuition. For example, the resonance structures shown in Figure 12–5 could be used to describe the HCl molecule by using the valence-bond theory; that is, a wave function can be written for each of the structures in Figure 12–5; the sum of these functions (suitably weighted) will yield a wave function that describes the electronic distribution in the HCl molecule as it exists in nature. However, since chlorine is more electronegative than hydrogen, it might be expected that the wave function for resonance structure IV in Figure 12–5 would not contribute significantly to the total wave function. Thus, intuition suggests that only the resonance

---

[4] The distinction between the resonance structures that are used to describe the molecule and the true structure of the molecule may be easier understood with the aid of an analogy (due to Wheland). A mule is a hybrid between a donkey and a horse. It is apparent that a mule is an independent entity, the characteristics of which might be described in terms of those of a donkey and a horse. A mule is not a horse part of the time and a donkey the other part. A herd of mules is not composed of donkeys and horses. So it is with the concept of resonance. The resonance structures themselves do not exist independently; they represent structures for which wave functions can be written. The point is to find a combination or a hybrid of the resonance structures which corresponds to the structure of the real molecule in question. For a lucid discussion of the concept of resonance the reader is directed to G. W. Wheland, *Resonance in Organic Chemistry* (New York: John Wiley and Sons, Inc., 1955), Chapter 1.

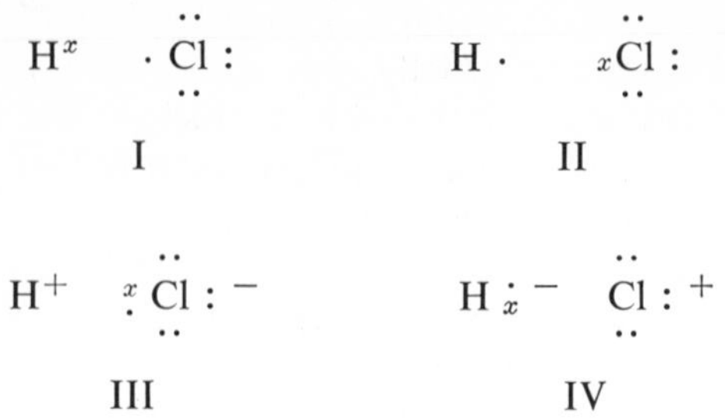

$$\overset{\cdot\cdot}{\text{H}^{x}} \quad \cdot \overset{\cdot\cdot}{\underset{\cdot\cdot}{\text{Cl}}} : \qquad\qquad \text{H} \cdot \quad {}_{x}\overset{\cdot\cdot}{\underset{\cdot\cdot}{\text{Cl}}} :$$

I   II

$$\text{H}^{+} \quad {}_{x}\overset{\cdot\cdot}{\underset{\cdot\cdot}{\text{Cl}}} : {}^{-} \qquad\qquad \text{H} \overset{\cdot}{\underset{x}{\cdot}} {}^{-} \quad \overset{\cdot\cdot}{\underset{\cdot\cdot}{\text{Cl}}} : {}^{+}$$

III   IV

FIGURE 12–5

The resonance structures for the HCl molecule. The electron originally associated with the hydrogen atom is designated by "x."

structures I, II, and III are important. It is apparent that structure III, since it represents the ionic extreme in electron distribution, contributes a certain amount of polarity to the hybrid structure, which, at least, is in qualitative agreement with the properties of the real HCl molecule. Similar valence-bond considerations for the structure of sodium chloride (Figure 12–6) suggest that structure VIII is the most important and that structures V, VI, and VII do not contribute significantly to the description of the true molecule. Thus HCl contains a predominantly covalent bond with some ionic character while NaCl is predominantly ionic with some covalent character.

The valence-bond method has been brought to a high degree of sophistication by Pauling[5] and his students and has been used to elucidate the constitution of a variety of complex chemical systems which include organic as well as inorganic examples.[6]

THE MOLECULAR ORBITAL METHOD

The distribution of electrons in a molecule can also be described by the molecular orbital method. The wave-mechanical model of an atom gives the distribution of electrons in terms of the electron density about the nucleus,

[5] Linus Pauling (1901–   ): Professor of Chemistry, California Institute of Technology. Pauling's research interests have touched on nearly every phase of chemistry. His early work was concerned with the determination of crystal structures using X-ray techniques; recently he has been engaged in a detailed crystallographic study of peptides and amino acids which has contributed to an understanding of the constitution of proteins. He is perhaps best known for his application of the methods of wave mechanics to elucidate the nature of the chemical bond; these studies led to the recognition of additivity of bond energies and covalent radii, the concept of resonance, and the development of electronegativity as a factor in determining covalent bond energies. In 1954 Pauling was awarded the Nobel Prize in chemistry, and eight years later he received the Nobel Peace Prize.

[6] For a thorough discussion of the valence-bond method and its application see Linus Pauling, *The Nature of The Chemical Bond* (Ithaca: Cornell University Press, 1960).

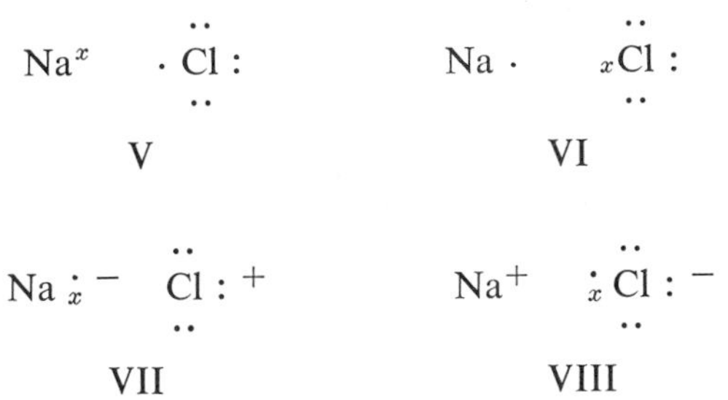

$$Na^x \quad \cdot \ddot{\underset{\cdot\cdot}{Cl}}: \qquad\qquad Na \cdot \quad _x\ddot{\underset{\cdot\cdot}{Cl}}:$$

V   VI

$$Na \overset{\cdot\cdot}{\underset{x}{:}}{}^- \quad \ddot{\underset{\cdot\cdot}{Cl}}:^+ \qquad\qquad Na^+ \quad \overset{\cdot\cdot}{\underset{x}{:}}\ddot{\underset{\cdot\cdot}{Cl}}:^-$$

VII   VIII

FIGURE 12–6

The resonance structures for sodium chloride.

certain volumes being more favored than others. The molecular orbital model of a compound involves the same principles. Each electron in a molecule is placed in a molecular orbital described by a certain wave function which has the same significance for the molecular system as it has for the atomic system. The molecular orbitals encompass all the nuclei in the molecule and represent the volumes in space in which electrons are permitted. As in atomic systems, each of the permitted energy levels in a molecule (the molecular orbitals) has a given energy and can be progressively filled (the Aufbau principle). Thus, the problem with the molecular orbital method is one of describing the shapes and energies of the possible molecular orbitals. As with the valence-bond method, this approximation starts from the atomic orbitals of the atoms involved in the bond. Therefore, if ψ_A represents the wave function for the valence atomic orbital of atom A, and ψ_B represents the wave function for the valence atomic orbital of atom B, then the wave function representing the molecular orbital containing the valence electrons of the molecule, A–B, is given by the combination.

$$\psi_{molecule} = \psi_A \pm C_B\psi_B \tag{2}$$

where C_B is a constant, chosen so that the energy of the molecular orbital is a minimum. It will be immediately recognized that this is essentially the same process used in the valence-bond method to combine wave functions for the various structures.

The mathematical combination of two atomic orbitals, according to Equation 2, yields two molecular orbitals which correspond to an addition and subtraction of the wave functions for the atomic orbitals. As in the case of the valence-bond theory, the addition of the atomic wave functions (ψ_+) yields a molecular orbital, the energy of which is lower than that obtained from the subtraction (ψ_-) of the atomic wave function (see Figure 12–7). The molecular orbital of the lower energy is called the bonding molecular orbital while that of the higher energy is called the antibonding molecular

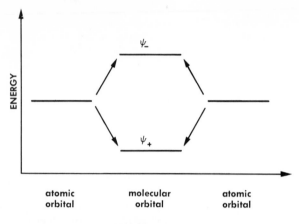

FIGURE 12–7

orbital. Electrons placed in bonding molecular orbitals occupy a volume of space within the internuclear region, screening the nuclei from each other (Figure 12–2), while electrons occupying antibonding molecular orbitals avoid the internuclear region, permitting the nuclei to repel each other. Thus, in a broad sense, electrons in antibonding molecular orbitals detract from the stability of the bond allowed to form by electrons occupying the corresponding bonding molecular orbitals.

These concepts can be readily illustrated by considering the molecular orbital descriptions of a series of simple homonuclear diatomic molecules such as H_2, Li_2, N_2, and F_2. For these molecules, only the $1s$, $2s$, and $2p$ atomic orbitals need be considered since these are the orbitals which contain the valence electrons. Figure 12–8 shows the shapes of the molecular orbitals that result from the combinations $\psi_{1s} \pm \psi_{1s}$, $\psi_{2s} \pm \psi_{2s}$, and $\psi_{2p} \pm \psi_{2p}$. It should be recalled that the set of p orbitals consists of three dumbbell-shaped clouds (cf. Figure 11–3), which means that p orbitals can combine in two different ways, i.e., "end on" ($\psi_{2p_x} \pm \psi_{2p_x} = \psi_{\sigma 2p}$) or "side by side" ($\psi_{2p_y} \pm \psi_{2p_y} = \psi_{\pi_y 2p}$ or $\psi_{2p_z} \pm \psi_{2p_z} = \psi_{\pi_z 2p}$). It should be noted that the "end on" combination of two p atomic orbitals gives a molecular orbital of the same shape as the combination of two s atomic orbitals. The symbols which represent the molecular orbitals given in Figure 12–8 reflect the symmetry of the molecular orbitals and the type of atomic orbital which was used to form the molecular orbitals in question. Thus, the Greek sigma, σ, is used to designate a molecular orbital that is symmetrical about a line drawn between the nuclei, analogous to the symmetry of the corresponding atomic orbital about the nucleus, designated by s. A similiar relationship occurs between atomic p orbitals and molecular π orbitals. The asterisk, *, designates antibonding molecular orbitals.

The relative order of energies for the molecular orbitals shown in Figure 12–8 has been determined from spectroscopic observations (much as in the case of atomic systems) and is given in Figure 12–9.

The distribution of electrons in the available molecular orbitals for a homonuclear diatomic molecule can be obtained. The Pauli exclusion principle limits each molecular orbital to a maximum of two electrons (spins paired).

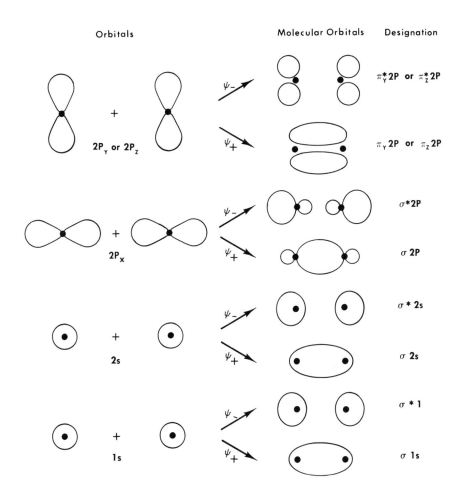

FIGURE 12–8

*The electron distribution for some molecular orbitals and the corresponding atomic orbitals from which they are formed. The Greek letters σ and π designate the molecular orbitals which arise from the combinations of atomic s and p orbitals; the asterisk, *, designates the antibonding molecular orbitals.*

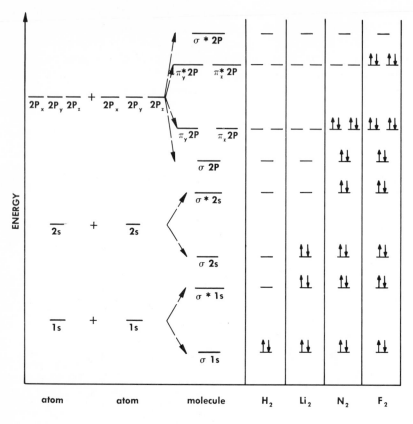

FIGURE 12–9

Thus, the two electrons in the hydrogen molecule, with their spins paired, occupy the lowest available molecular orbital which is a bonding orbital, $\sigma 1s$ (Figure 12–9); the shape of the electron cloud for the bonding electrons is given in Figure 12–10. The diatomic lithium molecule, Li_2 (a species known to exist in the vapor state), contains σ electrons distributed among the available molecular orbitals, as shown next in Figure 12–9. It is apparent from this distribution that the two electrons in the $\sigma 1s$ orbital cannot contribute to the nuclear bonding because their effect is cancelled by the two electrons in the antibonding $\sigma 1s$ orbital. Only two electrons, those in the $\sigma 2s$ orbital, remain to contribute to the bond. Thus the Li_2 molecule is held together by a sigma bond. Continuing our description of Figure 12–9, we see that the nitrogen molecule, N_2, contains fourteen electrons, six of which (three pairs) are in bonding orbitals (Figure 12–9); the remaining eight electrons do not contribute to the binding of the atoms since they are distributed in two bonding orbitals ($\sigma 1s$ and $\sigma 2s$) and two corresponding antibonding or-

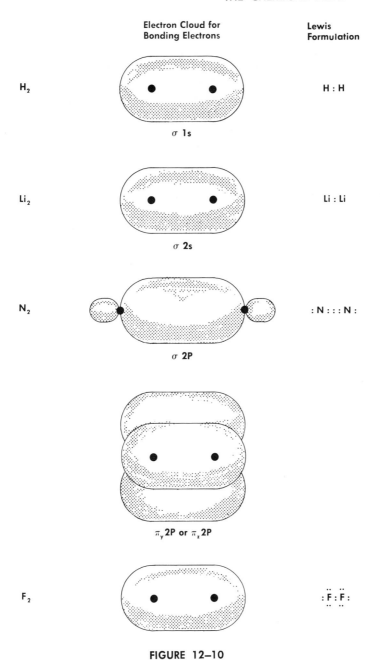

FIGURE 12–10

The distribution of bonding electrons in some simple diatomic molecules.

bitals ($\sigma 1s^*$ and $\sigma 2s^*$). The molecular orbital description of the triple bond in the N_2 molecule is also shown: the σ and π components of the triple bond have been separated for clarity. Finally, in the case of the fluorine molecule, F_2, the eighteen electrons in the system are distributed among the available molecular orbitals in such a way that only two electrons occupy bonding orbitals whose effects are not cancelled by electrons in the corresponding antibonding orbitals (Figure 12–9). Hence, the fluorine molecule, like lithium, is held together by a sigma bond (Figure 12–10). Thus we see that the formation of an electron-pair bond between two atoms, in the Lewis sense, corresponds to an increase in the electronic density between the atoms, which can be described by either the valence-bond method or the molecular orbital method. Similarly, it is possible to describe more complex molecules by using either of these two methods; their application not only yields the correct shapes for complex molecules but also provides good estimates of the energies involved in the formation of the molecules.

The ideas used to describe the covalent bond formed between two atoms have been presented in this chapter. It must be re-emphasized that a much more complex situation arises when an increasing number of atoms are bound together to form a molecule. The purposes of this volume would not be served, however, were we to enter into a detailed discussion of the numerous factors which emerge in the theoretical description of complex systems.

SUGGESTED READING

Companion, A. L. *Chemical Bonding*. New York: McGraw-Hill Book Company, Inc., 1964.

Pauling, L. "Valence Bond Theory in Coordination Chemistry," *Journal of Chemical Education*, **39**, 460 (1962).

Stewart, G. H., and Eyring, H. "The Principle of Minimum Bending of Orbitals," *Journal of Chemical Education*, **35**, 550 (1958).

Epilogue

We have returned full circle. The eloquent, penetrating arguments and the painstakingly beautiful experiments that were conceived to show matter as particulate rather than as continuous have led, in their full development, to a mathematical description which suggests the contrary, i.e., that every atom can occupy all of space. Let us take, for example, a universe consisting of an isolated hydrogen *molecule*. According to the modern description of a hydrogen *atom*, discrete orbitals cannot be precisely defined but, because of the uncertainty principle, must be described in terms of the volumes of space in which the electron most probably exists. That is, we can describe mathematically only the probability of finding an electron, but the nature of the mathematics involved leads to an answer which must include all of space, certain volumes being more favored than others. The pictures that are drawn to represent the most probable volumes in space where an electron may exist really represent the boundary within which the probability of finding an electron is very high, i.e., 90–95 per cent. It must be noted that the remainder of space is *not* excluded; the probability is very small that the electron will be found outside of these arbitrary boundaries. However, there is a finite probability of finding an electron in these outer regions, and, in principle, it can be calculated. Thus we see that each of the electrons in the two hydrogen *atoms* which comprise the hydrogen *molecule* in our hypothetical universe can exist throughout the universe, although the probability is very small that they will be found in places other than the immediate vicinity of their respective nuclei. For the hydrogen *molecule*, the area of maximum probability in which the two electrons can exist is found between the two nuclei. But a finite probability exists for finding these electrons, either paired or separately, in every part of our universe.

Thus, according to our modern description, the constituent parts of each bit of corpuscular matter can pervade the entire universe; in a sense we have returned to the suggestion of Aristotle that matter is continuous. It is true that our modern concept of matter arises from the mathematics used to describe it, but the latter alternative has been forced upon us by the uncertainty principle. To a first approximation, in ordinary chemical considerations, matter *is* corpuscular; however, in many instances the implications of the wave nature of matter become important. The development of the concept of chemical bonds has required a careful consideration of a variety of subjects; as a result, the interaction between atoms is now acknowledged to be basically electrical in nature. However, many of the details of this interaction are still in question and are being actively investigated today.

Affinity, 9 ff.
  elective, 17–20
  nature of, 19, 21
  tables of, 11–16, 20
Ammonia type, *see* Chemical types
Aristotle, 4
Atom(s): attraction between, 6–8
  Bohr-Sommerfeld model of, 85–89
  electron distribution in, 90–91
  electronic structure of, 79, 177–178
  geometrical arrangements of, 59
  Lewis theory of, 164
  mechanical linkages, 2
  nuclear, 71–76
  structure of, 79, 169
  Thomson model of, 79–84
Aufbau principle, 191
Avogadro, A., 23
Azimuthal quantum number, 173–174
Atomic number, 73–76
Atomic orbitals, 174, 193
  combination of, 191
  electron distribution in, 178
  energies of, 176
Atomic structure, 70 ff., 169
  Bohr's theory of, 85–88
  and electronic waves, 169
  Kossel theory of, 100, 101
  Lewis theory of, 99–103, 164
  stable, 83
  static model, 103–107, 164–165

Bergman, T. O., 13
  refined affinity tables, 13–16
Berthollet, C. L., 17
  clarification of affinity tables, 17–20
Berzelius, J. J., 23
  dualistic theory, 27–29
Bohr, N., 77
  postulate, 171
  theory of atomic structure, 77
Bond: coordinate covalent, 115
  electrical nature of, 26
  electron-pair, 111–114
  nature of, 2, 21, 25
  X-ray diffraction studies, 118–122

Boyle, R., 6
Bragg, W. H., 125
Bragg, W. L., 119

Carbon: stereochemistry of, 61–62
  tetrahedral valences, 60
Carbon-carbon: double bonds, 62
  triple bonds, 63
Cathode rays, 70
Chemical bond, 183 ff.
  Bohr model of, 143
  coordinate covalent, 151
  electrical nature of, 54–56, 131 ff.
  Heitler-London theory of, 183
  Kossel model of, 144
  Lewis theory of, 91, 111–114
  Lewis-Kossel theory of, 98 ff.
  molecular orbital method, 190
  recognition of, 124
  Stark model of, 142–143
  Thomson model of, 134
  valence-bond approximation, 185–190
  wave-mechanical model of, 183
Chemical formulas, 23–24, 32, 47–48
Chemical symbols, 31–32
Chemical types, 39 ff.
  ammonia type, 45, 46
  definition of, 40
  formulation of, 42–44
  hydrochloric acid type, 45, 46
  hydrogen type, 45, 46
  table of, 41
  water type, 45
Chromium, structure of, 128–129
Complex compounds, *see* Compounds
Composition, law of constant, 22–23
Compounds: complex, 150–151
  coordination, 150
  electron-deficient, 115
  ionic, 122–124
  molecule-forming, 122
  polar, 122
  unsaturated, 37
  valence, 122
Coordinate covalent bond, *see* Bond

Coordination compounds, 150
Couper, A. S., 52
    formulas, 53–54
Crookes, W., 70

Dalton, J., 23
Davisson, C. J., 167
Davy, H., 24
    electrolysis experiments, 24–26
de Broglie, L. V., 166
    "electronic waves," 166–167
Democritus, 2
Derivatives, concept of, 38
Dirac, P. A. M., 177
Double bonds, see Carbon-carbon
Dumas, J. B. A., 39
    theory of chemical types, 39–41

Effective atomic number (E.A.N.),
    153–154
Einstein, A., 166
Elective affinity, see Affinity
Electrolysis, 24, see also H. Davy
Electron-pair bond, see Bond
Electron(s), 70 ff.
    bonding, 194–195
    diffraction of, 167–169
    distribution
        Kossel, 100–101
        Lewis, 100–101
    dual nature of, 166
    extra-nuclear, 77
    pairing, 109
    pairs
        repulsion of, 156
        stereochemistry of, 154–163
        in valency shells, 157
    spin, 174–177
    valence, 99–100
    wave nature of, 164 ff.
    wave length of, 169–172
Electronegative bodies, 27–28
Electronic waves, intensity of, 171
Electrophile, 92, 93
Electropositive bodies, 27–28
Elements: classification of, 181
    electronic configuration of, 179
Epicurus, 2–3
Exclusion principle, Pauli, 176, 177, 193

Formula: chemical, 23, 32, 47–48
    rational, 51–52
    structural, 51–56

Frankland, E., 49
    and the valence concept, 49–51

Gay-Lussac, J. L., 29
Geoffroy, E., 9
    tables of affinity, 11–12
Gerhardt, C. F., 44
    chemical types, 44–46
Germer, L. H., 167
Gillespie, R. J., 156
Goudsmit, S. A., 176

Heisenberg, W., 171
    uncertainty principle, 171
Higgins, W., 55
Hydrochloric acid type, see Chemical
    types
Hydrogen spectrum, fine structure, 176
Hydrogen type, see Chemical types

Intermolecular forces, 126
Ionic compounds, 122
    forces in, 123
Isoelectronic species, 154
Isomerism, 33
Isomers, structure of, 60

Kekulé, F. A., 51
    "rational formulas," 51–52
Kernel, definition, 99
Kossel, W. L. J. P., 98

Laurent, A., 36
    substitution theory, 57–59
Law, periodic, 66
Law of constant composition, 22
LeBel, J. A., 60
Lemery, N., 5
Leucippus, 2
Lewis, G. N., 91
    atomic structure postulates, 99–103
Liebig, J., 35
Lucretius, 3

Magnetic quantum number, 173
Magnetism, 109
Mayow, J., 4
Mendeleev, D. I., 64
    periodic law, 64–68
Metals: forces in, 129
    structure of, 128

Molecular crystals, 125
Molecular geometry, early, 59
Molecular orbitals: antibonding, 191
  bonding, 191
  construction of, 190
  energies of, 193
  shapes of, 192
Molecular structure, 146 ff.
  electronic distribution in, 187
  Lewis theory of, 146 ff.
Molecule-forming compounds, 122
Molecules: geometry of, 146
  giant, 126
  shapes of, 157–159
Moseley, H. G. J., 71
  concept of atomic number, 73–76
  X-ray experiments, 71–76

Newton, I., 6
Non-polar molecule, 92–96
Nuclear atom, 71
Nyholm, R. S., 156

Octet theory, Lewis-Kossel, 98
Octet, expanded, 150
Orbitals: atomic, *see* Atomic orbital
  electronic density of, 175
  molecular, *see* Molecular orbital

Pauli, W. E., 176
Pauling, L., 190
Periodic classification, 181
Periodic law, 66
Periodic table: Mendeleev's, 67
Periodicity, 64 ff., 79 ff., 178
  and electronic structure, 89–91, 179
Perrin, J. B., 70
Polar compounds, *see* Compounds
Polar molecule, 92–96
Proust, J. L., 22
  law of constant composition, 22–23

Quantum mechanics, 164 ff.
Quantum numbers, 173–174
Quantum theory, 77

Radicals, 35
Ramsay, W., 132
Rational formulas, 51–52
Reactions, factors affecting, 16–18
  substitution, 29

Resonance, 189
  structures, 189
Rutherford, E., 71
Rydberg, J., 76
  wave number, 72

Schrödinger, E., 172
  equation, 172, 176, 184
  wave-mechanical concepts, 172–174
Sidgwick, N. V., 151
  theory of complex compounds, 151–152
Sommerfeld, A. J. W., 77; *see also* Atom
Spectra, X-ray, 71–73
Stark, J., 142; *see also* Bond
Stoner, E. C., 89
Structural formulas, 51–56
Structure, 31 ff.
  determination, 118 ff.
  types, 122
  See also Atomic structure
Substitution: reactions, 29
  theory, model for, 57–59
  theory of, 34 ff.
Symbols, chemical, 31

Thomson, J. J., 70
  model of chemical bond, 134–135
Triple bonds, *see* Carbon-carbon

Uhlenbeck, G. E., 176
Uncertainty principle, Heisenberg's, 171
Unsaturated compounds, *see* compounds

Valence, concept of, 49–51
  Lewis theory of, 97–98
Valence electrons, 99
Van Vleck, J. H., 180
Van't Hoff, J. H., 60
Volta, A., 24
von Helmholtz, H. L. F., 131
von Laue, M. T. F., 118

Williamson, A. W., 42
Wöhler, F., 35
Wyckoff, R. W. G., 121

X-Ray diffraction, 118–122
X-Ray spectra of elements, 71–76
X-Rays, 71